THOR IS BACK. WHILE STILL UNWORTHY OF LIFTING HIS HAMMER,
MJOLNIR, HE IS ONCE MORE THE GOD OF THUNDER.

JUST IN TIME, TOO. THE CITY OF ASGARDIA HAS BEEN DESTROYED, JANE FOSTER
IS STILL BATTLING CANCER AND ALL-FATHER ODIN IS BUSY TRYING TO RESTORE
OLD ASGARD TO ITS FORMER GLORY. SO IT'S UP TO THOR TO STOP MALEKITH'S ATTEMPT
TO CONQUER ALL OF THE TEN REALMS. BUT WITH THE RAINBOW BRIDGE SHATTERED,
HE HAS NO WAY OF TAKING THE FIGHT TO THE DARK ELF KING.

THOR NEEDN'T WORRY, HOWEVER — SOON THE WAR OF
THE REALMS WILL BE COMING TO EARTH…

IN THE FAR FUTURE, ALL-FATHER THOR AND HIS THREE
GRANDDAUGHTERS RESPARKED LIFE ON PLANET EARTH AFTER MILLENNIA
HAD LEFT IT BARREN. THE FIRST NEW HUMANS WERE NAMED "STEVE"
AND "JANE" AND GIVEN FREE REIN OVER THE NEW MIDGARD.

THOR CREATED BY **STAN LEE, LARRY LIEBER** & **JACK KIRBY**

COLLECTION EDITOR: **JENNIFER GRÜNWALD**
ASSISTANT MANAGING EDITOR: **MAIA LOY**
ASSISTANT EDITOR: **CAITLIN O'CONNELL**
EDITOR, SPECIAL PROJECTS: **MARK D. BEAZLEY**
VP PRODUCTION & SPECIAL PROJECTS: **JEFF YOUNGQUIST**
SVP PRINT, SALES & MARKETING: **DAVID GABRIEL**
EDITOR IN CHIEF: **C.B. CEBULSKI**

THOR BY JASON AARON VOL. 4. Contains material originally published in magazine form as THOR (2018) #1-11. First printing 2019. ISBN 978-1-302-92385-3. Published by MARVEL WORLDWIDE, INC., a subsidiary of MARVEL ENTERTAINMENT, LLC. OFFICE OF PUBLICATION: 1290 Avenue of the Americas, New York, NY 10104. © 2019 MARVEL No similarity between any of the names, characters, persons, and/or institutions in this magazine with those of any living or dead person or institution is intended, and any such similarity which may exist is purely coincidental. **Printed in Malaysia.** KEVIN FEIGE, Chief Creative Officer; DAN BUCKLEY, President, Marvel Entertainment; JOHN NEE, Publisher; JOE QUESADA, EVP & Creative Director; TOM BREVOORT, SVP of Publishing; DAVID BOGART, Associate Publisher & SVP of Talent Affairs; Publishing & Partnership; DAVID GABRIEL, VP of Print & Digital Publishing; JEFF YOUNGQUIST, VP of Production & Special Projects; DAN CARR, Executive Director of Publishing Technology; ALEX MORALES, Director of Publishing Operations; DAN EDINGTON, Managing Editor; SUSAN CRESPI, Production Manager; STAN LEE, Chairman Emeritus. For information regarding advertising in Marvel Comics or on Marvel.com, please contact Vit DeBellis, Custom Solutions & Integrated Advertising Manager, at vdebellis@marvel.com. For Marvel subscription inquiries, please call 888-511-5480. **Manufactured between 12/20/2019 and 3/2/2020 by TIEN WAH PRESS, JOHOR BAHRU, JOHOR, MALAYSIA.**

THOR

WRITER
JASON AARON

ISSUES #1-4

ARTIST
MIKE DEL MUNDO

COLOR ASSISTS, #1 & #3-4
MARCO D'ALFONSO

"THE GRACE OF THOR" ARTIST
CHRISTIAN WARD

ISSUES #5-6

ARTIST
CHRISTIAN WARD

ISSUE #7

ARTIST
TONY MOORE

COLOR ARTIST
JOHN RAUCH

ISSUES #8-10

ARTIST
MIKE DEL MUNDO

COLOR ARTISTS
MIKE DEL MUNDO
WITH **MARCO D'ALFONSO** (#10)

ISSUE #11

ARTIST
LEE GARBETT

COLOR ARTIST
ANTONIO FABELA

LETTERER
VC's JOE SABINO

COVER ART
MIKE DEL MUNDO (#1-4 & #7-11)
& **ESAD RIBIĆ** (#5-6)

ASSOCIATE EDITOR
SARAH BRUNSTAD

EDITOR
WIL MOSS

EXECUTIVE EDITOR
TOM BREVOORT

THOR # 1 VARIANT
BY **ESAD RIBIĆ**

GOD OF THUNDER REBORN

JUGGERNAUT!!!

I WAS NOT BORN WITH A HAMMER IN MY HAND!

BUT I *WAS* BORN WITH THUNDER IN MY HEART!

RAGING THUNDER!

I AM THE LORD OF THE LIVING STORM, NO MATTER THE WEAPON I HOLD!

BUT IF 'TIS *HAMMERS* YOU WISH FOR, JUGGERNAUT, YOU SON OF A GOBLIN, THEN TRY THIS ONE ON FOR--

CRACK

um...

HA HA HAA!
THOR? YOU DEAD? TELL ME IF YOU DEAD.
I LIVE, SCREWBEARD.
BY ALL THE GODS, DO I LIVE.
GOOD. ONLY LITTLE SURPRISING. YOU BLUDGEON HIM VIGOROUSLY THEN? THIS JUGGLER PERSON?
THE JUGGERNAUT. AND AYE, THERE WAS INDEED MUCH BLUDGEONING.
AT LEAST ENOUGH FOR ME TO ESCAPE WITH THE WARLOCK'S EYE.
OLD ASGARD.
WHICH HAMMER YOU USE? WAS BIG ONE, YES? HULK-SMITER?
I HAD TO USE THEM ALL.
AND ALL WERE VERY FINE, I SURE? NO ONE FORGES WEAPONS LIKE DWARVES OF NIDAVELLIR.
THESE HAMMERS WILL LAST FOR MUCH BLUDGEONING YET TO COME, YES?
THOR?

YOU BREAK ALL HAMMERS?!

TECHNICALLY 'TWAS JUGGERNAUT'S *FACE* THAT BROKE THEM...BUT AYE.

YOU SAY MAKE HAMMERS, SCREWBEARD AND FRIENDS WORK MANY NIGHTS MAKING BEST HAMMERS IN ALL TEN REALMS.

ODIN PUT *SPELLS* ON ALL. NO ONE SLEEP. NO ONE EVEN HAVE TIME FOR BEING DRUNKEN.

AND YOU BREAK ALL IN ONE DAY. FIGHTING JUGGLER.

I'M SORRY, MY FRIEND, BUT I'LL NEED MORE.

"NEED MORE," HE SAY. THOR BECOMING GOD OF BEING PAIN IN DWARF BACKSIDE!

THEY MUST BE STRONGER. WE NEED PURER *URU.*

AH YES, MOST VERY WONDERFUL IDEA. WHY SCREWBEARD NEVER THINKING OF THIS?

MAYBE 'CAUSE URU NOT GROW ON TREES!

SCREWBEARD'S HAD A LOT OF DYNAMITE GO OFF NEAR HIS HEAD OVER THE YEARS, BUT HE'S ACTUALLY NOT AS STUPID AS HE LOOKS.

THE OLD ASGARDIAN MINES HAVE ALL RUN DRY. IT WOULD SEEM THERE ISN'T MUCH URU LEFT IN EXISTENCE.

BUT IF THERE'S MORE HERE UNDER THIS GROUND, I SWEAR TO YOU, THOR, AS A SWORN BROTHER IN THE *LEAGUE OF REALMS,* UD THE TROLL WILL FIND IT.

WE'LL SCROUNGE UP WHAT WEAPONS WE HAVE. FOR NOW, I SUGGEST YOU MAKE THOSE LAST.

MJOLNIR DID NOT LAST.

BUILD AS MANY AS YOU CAN, MY BROTHERS. AND I'LL BRING YOU ENOUGH MEAD TO DROWN A DRAGON.

THERE'S *WAR* IN THE REALMS. WAR UNLIKE ANY WE'VE EVER SEEN.

I'M GOING TO NEED ALL THE HAMMERS I CAN GET.

GAGH! ENOUGH TO DROWN A DRAGON, HE SAY. I SETTLE FOR ENOUGH TO DRUNKEN A DWARF.

THIS WHAT WE GET FOR BEING ON ASGARDIA WHEN BIFROST GO BOOM!

OH, STOP WHINING LIKE AN ELF AND TRY WORKING LIKE A TROLL FOR ONCE. WE CAN DRINK WHEN WE'RE IN HEL.

I SURROUNDED BY GODS AND BEST FRIEND IS TROLL. THIS ALREADY HEL.

I HOPE THE REPAIRS TO THE *RAINBOW BRIDGE* ARE FARING BETTER THAN MY HAMMERS, HEIMDALL.

ALL THE SHARDS THAT COULD BE FOUND FLOATING IN THE SPACEWAYS HAVE BEEN GATHERED.

BUT 'TIS NO SIMPLE MATTER TO PIECE THEM BACK TOGETHER. LET ALONE *RECHARGE* THEM.

I DON'T NEED EYES TO SEE YOUR UNEASE, ODINSON. KNOW THAT I FEEL THE SAME, MY PRINCE.

WITHOUT THE POWER OF THE BIFROST, WE ARE CUT OFF FROM THE REST OF THE REALMS, WHERE MALEKITH'S WAR NO DOUBT RAGES ON.

YOUR EYES... SO YOU STILL CANNOT...

MY ALL-SEEING EYES WERE YET ANOTHER CASUALTY OF THE MANGOG'S RAMPAGE. I AM AFRAID WE STILL HAVE NO IDEA HOW THE OTHER REALMS ARE FARING.

AND HOW IS IT THAT *WE* ARE FARING?

WE GODS NOW LIVE IN PAIN AND SQUALOR, IN THE RUINS OF OUR FORMER GLORY. YET STILL WE LIVE.

EITHER WE WILL SURVIVE AND REBUILD, OR ELSE FACE THE FINAL TWILIGHT AND PRAY FOR VALHALLA.

THIS HAS ALWAYS BEEN THE WAY. SINCE WELL BEFORE THE TIME OF OUR FATHERS' FATHERS.

AYE, MY FRIEND...

"AND SPEAKING OF FATHERS..."

THE ENCHANTMENTS WORKED, I HEAR.

YOU *FLEW* ONCE MORE, LIKE THE THUNDER GOD OF OLD.

NOT EXACTLY LIKE OF OLD. BUT AYE, FATHER, I DID FLY. AND I DID THUNDER.

THOUGH I AM AFRAID WE WILL NEED MORE HAMMERS. AND THUS MORE OF THOSE ENCHANTMENTS OF YOURS.

I FIGURED AS MUCH. YOU WERE ALWAYS GOOD AT SMASHING THINGS. ESPECIALLY WHEN THEY WERE MINE.

BUT THOSE OLD DAYS NOW SEEM SO VERY DISTANT. I FEAR THE GREAT WOUNDS OF OUR RECENT TRIALS WILL NOT BE AS EASILY HEALED AS IN TIMES PAST.

I THOUGHT YOU NEVER WARMED TO ASGARDIA. HAD TOO MUCH THE STENCH OF *STARK* ON IT, YOU ALWAYS SAID.

I WAS NOT REFERRING TO ASGARDIA.

YOU'VE *SEEN* HER?

AYE, FATHER.

LOOKING GOOD, THOR.

HOW'D IT FEEL, THE FIRST DAY BACK ON THE JOB?

DAMN RIGHT I DO.

YOU KNOW BETTER THAN ANYONE HOW IT FELT, *JANE FOSTER.*

AND YOU RECOVERED THE WARLOCK'S EYE. NICE WORK.

NOW I'VE GOT ANOTHER LEAD FOR YOU. THERE ARE REPORTS FROM THE SOUTHERN OCEAN OF THE WATERS BUBBLING AND BOILING. JUST MY GUT, BUT IT COULD BE OUR MISSING *GEM OF INFINITE SUNS.*

AYE, COULD BE.

THAT'S A... NICE GOLDEN *HAMMER* YOU GOT THERE...

HOW'S THE VELOCITY ON IT? DOES IT DRIFT TO THE LEFT A LITTLE LIKE MJOLNIR DID? I DON'T SUPPOSE I COULD...

...TOUCH IT...

...JUST A LITTLE?

ARE YOU CANCER-FREE AND NO ONE TOLD ME?

THE DOCTORS SAY I'M MAKING GREAT PROGRESS.

THEN PLEASE TRY AND KEEP IT THAT WAY.

SO THAT'S A...

NO, YOU MAY NOT TOUCH MY HAMMER.

...

YOU JUST WANTED ME TO SAY THAT, DIDN'T YOU?

HEH. WELCOME BACK, THOR. AND SHE'S UPSTAIRS, BY THE WAY.

FISHIE?
FISHIE FOR
THORI?

THORI
MURDER WITH
MOUTH NOW?

FLOPP!

BE MY
GUEST, DOG.
ONE MOMENT,
THOUGH.

THE GEM OF INFINITE
SUNS HAS OFFICIALLY
BEEN RECOVERED.

AND I OFFICIALLY
NEED A DRINK.

THORI
GOOD DOG,
MASTER! THORI
GUARD MASTER'S
HOME FROM ALL
INVASION!

I SAID... I'M NOT HERE TO FIGHT.

FOR ALL THE BLASTED GOOD THAT WILL DO ME.

LIES!

MORE OF YOUR CRAVEN LIES!

THOR, LISTEN TO ME. I'M NOT YOUR ENEMY.

WELL, I MEAN, I AM. BUT NOT THIS TIME IN PARTICULAR.

I SWEAR I'M NOT THE MONSTER YOU MIGHT THINK. NO MATTER WHAT LADY FREYJA MIGHT HAVE--

RRGGGH!

HHK!

SAY HER NAME AGAIN, AND I PROMISE YOU WILL DROWN IN YOUR OWN JOTUNN BLOOD.

HELP. I... GGHK...

I'M HERE TO HELP.

I CAN DO WHAT EVEN THE ALL-FATHER CAN'T. I CAN HELP YOU... END THE WAR.

GUUGH!

ZZOOOOOMMM

INTRUDER! INTRUDER!

BIT LATE FOR THAT, DOG.

THORI. DON'T SUPPOSE YOU COULD HELP OUT YOUR OLD MASTER?

THORI MURDER LOKI NOW, MASTER?

PERHAPS.

WHY WOULD YOU HELP ME?

I COULD ANSWER THAT QUESTION, BUT NO MATTER WHAT I SAID, YOU'D JUST DISMISS IT AS A LIE.

ALL I'LL SAY IS, I WANT SOMETHING IN RETURN. SOMETHING YOU HAVE HERE ON THIS BOAT.

THE LOST WEAPONS. YOU'RE AS MAD AS YOUR FROST GIANT FATHER IF YOU THINK I'D EVER WILLINGLY LET YOU LAY A FINGER ON ANY OF THOSE WEAPONS.

I NEVER SAID IT WAS A WEAPON. BUT I'LL ONLY NAME MY PRICE ONCE YOU'VE COMPLETED YOUR JOURNEY.

WHAT DAMN JOURNEY?

FRIGG IS RIGHT. THIS IS A BAD IDEA. I'LL HURL THE CREATURE INTO THE DEPTHS OF SPACE.

YOU DO THAT AND IT'LL DIE! ALL-GRANDFATHER, TRUST ME! JUST LET IT GO!

DON'T THINK...I HAVE MUCH CHOICE IN THAT ANYWAY.

ATLI, BE READY WITH YOUR AX, GIRL!

THAT WON'T BE NECESSARY.

IT'S WORKING. IT'S ACTUALLY EATING THAT STUFF. WHAT THE HEL IS THAT STUFF AGAIN?

AN ANCIENT RECIPE I UNCOVERED, MEANT TO REPLICATE THE TASTE AND TEXTURE OF MEAT. IT'S PROCESSED WHEAT GLUTEN MOSTLY.

IN OTHER WORDS, WE JUST TURNED THE UNIVERSE'S LAST SPACE SHARK INTO A VEGETARIAN.

AND INTO OUR PET! I NAME IT DEATH MOUTH!

YOU GIRLS NEVER FAIL TO ASTOUND ME. WELL DONE, GODDESSES OF THUNDER.

THANKS, GRANDFATHER, BUT THE SHARK ISN'T THE REAL PROBLEM HERE.

THE FACT THAT IT HAD TO SWIM SO FAR IN ORDER TO FIND MEAT MEANS THAT--

HOLD, ELLISIV. I HEAR...

PRAYERS COMING FROM NEW MIDGARD. PRAYERS FOR...

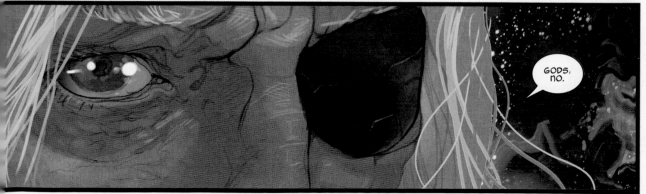

GODS, NO.

SHE'S BEEN WEAK FOR DAYS. THIS MORNING, SHE COULD NOT RISE AND BEGAN ASKING FOR...

...FOR HER CREATOR.

TELL HER HE HAS COME.

SHE KNOWS.

SHE'S NOT TOO OLD OR DEAD TO FEEL THE PRESENCE OF HER GOD. GREETINGS, MY LORD. PLEASE FORGIVE ME IF I DO NOT RISE.

NONSENSE. YOU'VE EARNED YOUR REST, MY LADY. BUILDING A NEW WORLD FROM NOTHING IS NO EASY TASK.

YOU WERE THE BUILDER. MY HUSBAND AND I MERELY THE CARETAKERS.

I MISS HIM, LORD THOR. I HAVE BEEN TOO LONG WITHOUT MY BEAUTIFUL STEVE.

TOO LONG, PERIOD. TWO HUNDRED SEVENTY-FIVE YEARS IS ENOUGH LIFE FOR ANYONE.

NOT FOR YOU.

NOT IF YOU WISH IT.

JUST AS I ONCE GAVE YOU LIFE, I COULD NOW GIVE YOU MORE. MORE OF MY POWER TO KEEP YOU ALIVE.

I SAY THEE...NAY, MY LORD.

JUST SAY THE WORD, LADY JANE, AND YOUR GOD WILL MAKE IT SO.

IS SHE...

SHE'S GONE.

YOUR MOTHER HAS LEFT US.

JANE, THE MOTHER OF THE NEW EARTH.

HALLOWED BE HER NAME.

WE WILL NEVER SEE HER LIKE AGAIN.

A GREAT WOMAN IS DEAD.

TWO HUNDRED AND SEVENTY-FIVE YEARS AGO, I MADE HER FROM DUST AND CLAY. BUT LIKE MOST ANY CHILD, SHE VERY QUICKLY OUTGREW HER PARENT.

SHE BROUGHT LIFE AND LOVE TO WHAT HAD BEEN A DEAD EARTH FOR CENTURIES, IN A WAY I NEVER COULD.

SHE WAS AN ALL-MOTHER. THE VERY LAST ALL-MOTHER.

NO. PERHAPS NOT THE LAST.

GRANDFATHER. WE MUST TALK.

NOT NOW, ELLISIV. LET ME MOURN.

WITH ALL DUE RESPECT, ALL-FATHER, IF WE DON'T SPEAK NOW, THERE WILL BE MUCH MORE MOURNING TO COME.

NOT THIS AGAIN. GRANDDAUGHTER, YOU SPEND TOO MUCH TIME GAZING AT THE STARS AND NOT ENOUGH TIME FLYING AMONG THEM.

WHAT STARS? I'VE CHECKED AND RECHECKED MY OBSERVATIONS. I KNOW WHAT'S HAPPENING OUT THERE. EVEN IF YOU WON'T--

I SAID NOT NOW, AND I MEANT IT. NOW CEASE THIS--

WHERE'S YOUR HAMMER, GRANDFATHER?

YOU HAVEN'T CARRIED IT FOR DAYS. WHERE IS IT?

GET BACK TO ASGARD, YOUNG LADY. YOU ARE CONFINED TO QUARTERS. ALL-FATHER'S ORDERS.

AND DON'T YOU DARE SAY A WORD OF THIS NONSENSE TO YOUR--

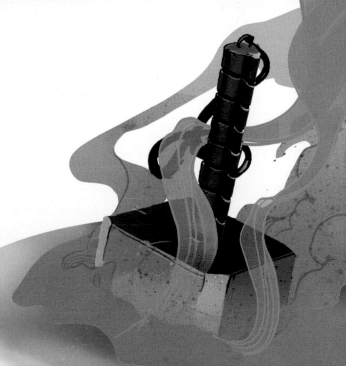

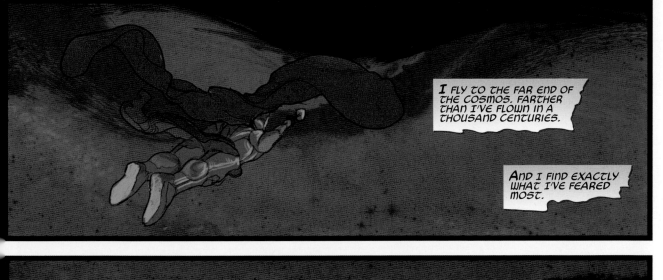

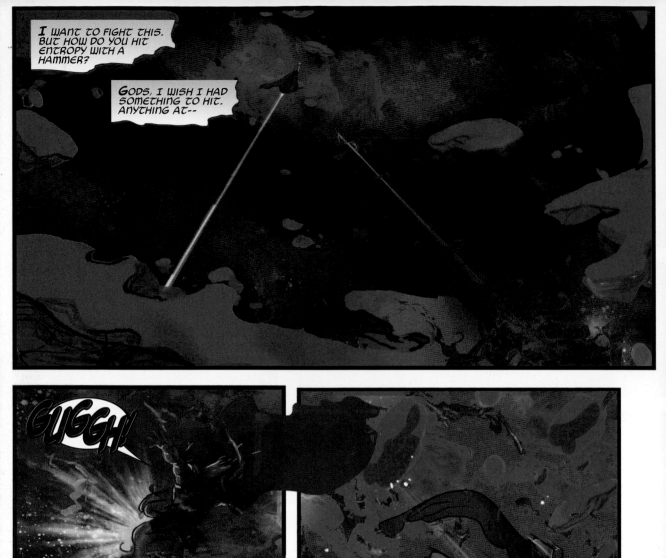

2

THE ODINSON BOYS RIDE AGAIN

"LISTEN, BROTHER. CAN YOU HEAR THAT BEAUTIFUL CHORUS?

"ALONG THE BANKS OF THE VENOMOUS RIVER *GJÖLL*, THE LOST SOULS BURIED UP TO THEIR NECKS ARE WAILING THEIR HYMNS OF SORROW AS THE BLOODY ICE-WAVES COME CRASHING IN.

"IN *NÁSTROND*, ALONG THE SHORE OF CORPSES, THE GREAT DRAGON *NÍDHÖGG* ROARS AND FEASTS ON THE FLESH OF OATH-BREAKERS.

"AND THE GLEAMING SNOW GARDENS THAT SURROUND *HVERGELMIR*, THE HOLY WELLSPRING OF ALL RIME AND COLD, ECHO WITH ANCIENT DIRGES AND LAMENTATIONS AS GREAT PYRES ARE LIT TO WELCOME THE FRESHLY FALLEN.

"THE DAMNED AND BLESSED ALIKE. THE LOWLY AND DIVINE. THE LOST AND ETERNALLY VALIANT.

"I'D LIKE TO THINK THOSE PYRES WERE ALSO LIT FOR *MY* RETURN.

"BUT WE KNOW THAT ISN'T TRUE, DON'T WE?

"HEL HAS *FORGOTTEN* ALL ABOUT ME."

CHOO! CHOOO!

BURN THE DEAD THINGS! ALL HAIL THE QUEEN OF CINDERS!
TOO LATE! FIREPEDES INCOMING!
ROTTEN FLAMING BASTARDS. YOU SEEK TO CONQUER HEL, SONS OF MUSPEL?!
THERE'S A DEAD MAN HERE WHO SAYS THEE NAY!
DOOT DOOT DOOT DOOT
I SEE DEATH HASN'T CHANGED THE EXECUTIONER.
GET IN THE TRUCK! HURRY OR WE'LL HAVE THEIR WHOLE ARMY DOWN ON OUR HEADS!
WAIT! I SHALL NOT ABANDON MY VESSEL!
YOU CANNOT BE SERIOUS. THAT IS THE UGLIEST BOAT I HAVE EVER SEEN. AND HERE WE MAKE THEM FROM THE FINGERNAILS OF THE DEAD. YOU WOULD RISK YOUR LIFE FOR THAT HEAP OF RUBBISH?
THAT HEAP OF RUBBISH IS ALL I HAVE, BALDER!
LIFE HAS CLEARLY NOT BEEN KIND TO YOU OF LATE, BROTHER. BUT WE CAN'T--
OH, STAND ASIDE AND LET A SORCERER WORK.
TOOTHGNASHER

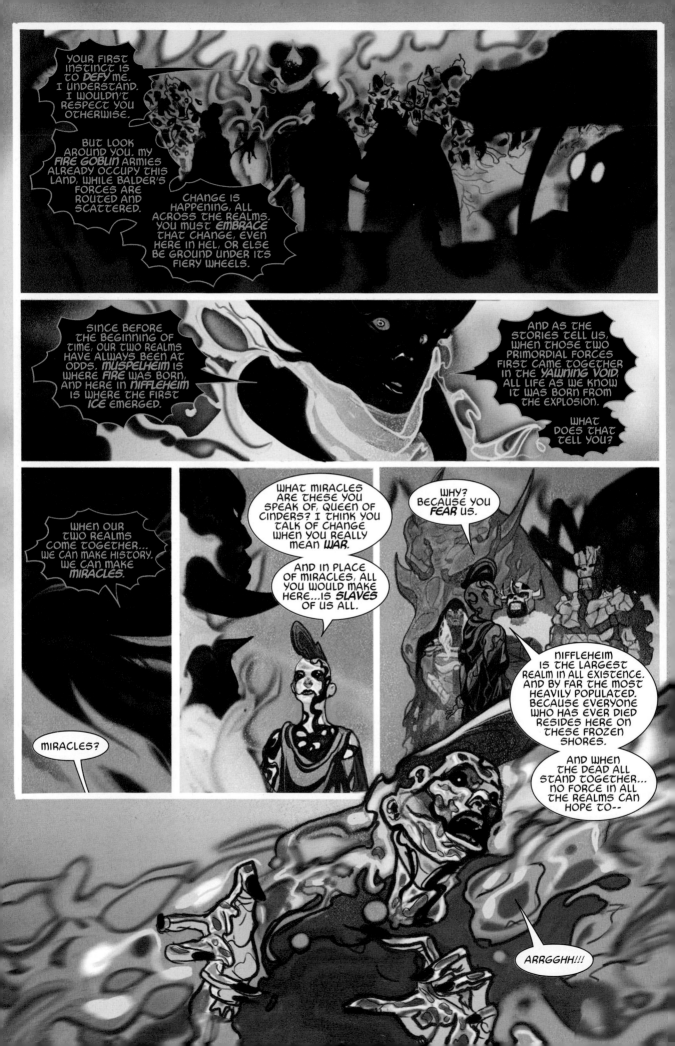

WE MAY HAVE FAILED TO UNCOVER THE LOCATION OF SINDR'S MEETING WITH THE CHIEFTAINS, BUT KARNILLA AND I DID LEARN SOMETHING *ELSE* OF NOTE FROM THE GOBLIN PATROLS WE INTERCEPTED.

THE ARMY OF MUSPELHEIM HAS ACQUIRED A SUPREMELY POWERFUL *NEW* WEAPON.

IT'S BEING TRANSPORTED BY TRAIN AS WE SPEAK, ALONG THE *HELVEGR.* IT SHOULD BE NEAR THE BRIDGE *GJALLERBRU* BY NOW.

WHAT IS THIS WEAPON?

WE DON'T KNOW. BUT THE GOBLINS SPOKE OF IT WITH GREAT FEAR AND AWE.

THAT SOUNDS LIKE SOMETHING WE SHOULD HAVE MOUNTED ON THE BACK OF OUR *TRUCK.*

SO WE AGREE? WE'LL TAKE THIS CARAVAN AND USE THE QUEEN OF CINDERS' OWN WEAPON *AGAINST* HER.

I WILL FOLLOW YOU ANYWHERE, KING OF HEL.

BLESS YOU, BROTHER. IT WILL BE AN HONOR TO FIGHT ALONGSIDE YOUR THUNDER ONCE MORE.

HA! THE *ODINSON BROTHERS,* TOGETHER AGAIN!

BY ALL THE GODS, THERE WILL BE MORE SMITING AND DRINKING THAN HEL HAS EVER SEEN!

AND MORE MANLY HUGS!

HGGK!

GODS, IF IT'S GOING TO BE LIKE THIS THE ENTIRE TIME, I MAY WELL GO BACK TO BEING A VILLAIN.

HOW'S *AMORA?* SHE EVER ASK ABOUT ME? SHE'S ON YOUR SIDE, RIGHT, LOKI?

THERE *ARE* NO SIDES WHEN IT COMES TO LOKI. ONLY *LOKI.*

MAKE YOUR PEACE WITH HEL, PRINCE OF LIES. IF I HAVE MY WAY, YOU'LL NEVER LIVE LONG ENOUGH TO LEAVE.

I WOULD... TAKE A HUG.

NOT THAT ANYONE'S OFFERING.

MAKE SURE ALL IS READY, SKURGE. WE LEAVE AT ONCE.

HOW DID YOU COME BY SUCH VEHICLES, BALDER, HERE IN THE FROZEN WILDS OF HEL?

IT'S NOT JUST THE DEAD WHO WASH UP ON THESE SHORES. THINGS FROM ALL THE REALMS FALL THROUGH TO NIFFLEHEIM.

DIG INTO THESE SNOWS, AND THERE'S NO TELLING WHAT YOU MIGHT FIND. AND WE'LL NEED EVERY BIT OF IT WE CAN SALVAGE...

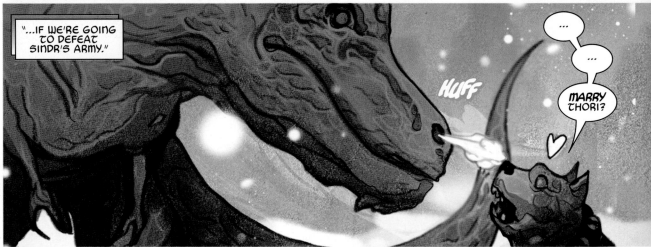

"...IF WE'RE GOING TO DEFEAT SINDR'S ARMY."

...

...

HUFF

MARRY THORI?

THOR? A WORD IF YOU PLEASE?

THAT ALWAYS SOUNDS LIKE A THREAT COMING FROM *YOU*, LOKI.

NO THREATS. ONLY A WARNING.

TRUST TYR AT YOUR PERIL.

I KNOW HE'S YOUR BROTHER. BUT BELIEVE IT OR NOT, EVEN BROTHERS CAN BETRAY YOU.

BETRAY ME TO WHOM? AN ODINSON WOULD NEVER SIDE WITH THE SPAWN OF SURTUR.

TYR'S BEEN IN HEL A LONG TIME. HIS ALLEGIANCES ARE NOT NECESSARILY TO THE LIVING...

...OR TO THOSE HE ONCE CALLED KIN.

WORRY MORE ABOUT YOUR *OWN* ALLEGIANCES, LOKI.

AS WILL I.

THE WATERS OF THE GJOLL RIVER ARE CRUSHINGLY COLD AND DEATHLY VENOMOUS.

THE DEEPER I SWIM, THE MORE I FEEL THE LIFE FLOWING OUT OF ME. BUT IF I DIE, I DIE TO END THE WAR.

AND I DO SO GLADLY.

UNTIL I SEE WHAT IT IS WE'VE JUST UNLEASHED. AND THEN I REALIZE...

...WE'VE JUST STARTED ANOTHER WAR OF OUR OWN.

UH-OH. BIG UGLY FISH.

THAT'S NO FISH, THORI...

3

A LOVELY DAY IN HEL FOR A WEDDING

SKURGE! WHAT ARE YOU DOING? YOUR KING NEEDS YOU!

YEAH, I THINK I'M JUST GONNA SEE HOW THIS ONE PLAYS OUT FIRST.

IF BALDER LOSES, I CALL DIBS ON THE TRUCK.

SO YOU THINK YOU'RE NOT A PUNY LITTLE BOY ANYMORE, EH? COULD'VE FOOLED ME.

GUUGH!

I SEE A LOKI STILL QUIVERING IN THE SHADOWS OF HIS OWN MIGHTY FATHERS, TOO WEAK TO EVER BE HIS OWN MAN.

YOU EVEN CHOOSE TO WEAR A WHELP'S FACE! YOU ARE EVER THE CHILD PLAYING AT CHILDISH GAMES, LITTLE LAUFEYSON.

BUT THE GAMES OF WAR ARE MEANT FOR GROWN-ASS GODS!

CHOMP!

WHAT--

THORI NOT SURE WHO ON WHICH SIDE NOW! SO THORI MURDER EVERYONE, SORT IT OUT LATER!

WHAT WAS IT YOU WERE SAYING, BROTHER, ABOUT WEARING A WHELP'S FACE?

NO! YOU... YOU WOULDN'T! BROTHER, BE REASONABLE! NOT MY BEAUTIFUL WHISKERS!

ANYTHING BUT THE MUSTACHE!

I WILL SLURP YOU UP LIKE A BOWL OF SOUP, YOU MISERABLE BASTARD! FENRIS IS HAVING UNCLE FOR DINNER!

UH, FENRIS, I WOULDN'T GO BACK IN THIS *RIVER* IF I WERE--

THE REALMS ARE BURNING, AND I CANNOT STOP THE WAR FROM RAGING.

THE EONS WILL ROLL BY ONE AFTER ANOTHER UNTIL ALL THE STARS HAVE GROWN COLD, AND I WILL STILL BE THERE, MOURNING EVERYONE I HAVE EVER LOVED BUT COULDN'T SAVE.

THERE IS NO PLACE FOR YOU HERE ON THESE SHORES, THE WATERS WHISPER.

LIKE I COULDN'T STOP ASGARDIA FROM EXPLODING IN THE SUN. ALONG WITH MY HAMMER. THE ONE I COULDN'T LIFT ANYMORE ANYWAY.

NO GOD IS WORTHY. MOST ESPECIALLY NOT ME.

THE IMMORTAL THOR IS *UNWORTHY* OF EVEN DYING.

BUT THAT IS THE RIVER TALKING. THE POISON WATERS OF GJOLL. TO SURVIVE ITS EMBRACE, I MUST...THINK *HAPPIER* THOUGHTS.

LIKE MEAD. WENCHES. WENCHES WITH MEAD.

SMITING TROLLS. SMITING DARK ELVES. SMITING FATHER. STEALING FATHER'S MEAD.

DRINKING WITH STARK AND ROGERS. RACING COMETS. SMITING COMETS. SMITING FENRIS.

COLD ALE AND A WARM HAMMER. THUNDER IN MY EARS.

JANE FOSTER IS ALIVE.

AND SO THE HEL AM I.

HELA, DON'T BE A FOOL. WE'RE NOT THE ONES SETTING THIS REALM ABLAZE. *SINDR* IS THE REAL ENEMY HERE.

ONE USURPER AT A TIME!

FENRIS, WHERE ARE YOU, BROTHER? YOUR MEAL GROWS COLD!

NO, I'M ONLY GETTING WARMED UP, YOU THORN-FACED--

VRAAKKRRBB

I CAN'T BELIEVE YOU TALKED THEM INTO THIS.

HELA AND BALDER BOTH KNEW THERE WAS NO OTHER WAY TO UNITE THE REALM. ESPECIALLY WITH SINDR'S ARMY CLOSING IN.

YOU OFFERED A SOLUTION THAT AVOIDED UNDUE BLOODSHED, BROTHER. I'M *SURPRISED* AT YOU.

I'M A BIT SURPRISED AT MYSELF, TO BE HONEST.

BUT I FEAR IT WON'T BE ENOUGH. NOT AGAINST SINDR'S ARMY.

THE DEAD SOULS IN *NIFFLEHEIM* ARE WITHOUT NUMBER, THOR. IF THIS *MARRIAGE* TRULY SUCCEEDS IN UNITING THEM, HEL WILL HAVE AN INSURMOUNTABLE FORCE.

AYE, BUT NONE OF THOSE DEAD WERE GREAT WARRIORS IN LIFE. AND IT'S WARRIORS WE NEED.

WE NEED THE *EINHERJAR*.

WE NEED THE WARRIORS OF *VALHALLA*.

IS IT **DONE** THEN, KARNILLA?

NOT YET.

I THOUGHT YOU WERE SUPPOSED TO SAVE YOUR **BLUBBERING** FOR THE END?

THIS **IS** THE END. FOR **ME**, AT LEAST. THE END OF A FOOLISH DREAM I'VE CHERISHED FOR FAR TOO LONG.

OKAY, SURE. WHATEVER THAT MEANS.

YOU ARE A CALLOUS SOUL, SKURGE. HAVEN'T YOU EVER KNOWN LOVE?

OH AYE. I'VE LOVED. AS TRULY AND DEEPLY AS ANY MAN.

IT WAS CALLED THE **BLOODAXE**.

I AM NOT IN THE MOOD TO BE **MOCKED**, EXECUTIONER.

WELL LOOK, DON'T BLAME ME. YOU'RE THE **NORNQUEEN**, RIGHT? YOU KNOW BETTER THAN ANYONE THAT OUR FATES ARE UP TO THE **NORNS**. BLAME THEM.

THE **NORNKEEP** HAS FALLEN. THE NORNS ARE NO MORE.

OUR FATES ARE OUR OWN NOW. FOR BETTER OR WORSE.

OH.

WELL, THAT EXPLAINS WHY EVERYTHING **SUCKS** NOW.

4

WAR IS HEL

THE GATES OF VALHALLA.

YOU'RE A FINE SWORDSMAN, BALDER, BUT IT TAKES MORE THAN A STRONG SWORD HAND TO WEAR THAT HEL-CROWN!

ONLY A TRUE KILLER DESERVES TO RULE THE LAND OF THE DEAD!

GAGH! NEVER KNEW IT'D BE HARDER STAYING IN ONE PIECE WHEN I WAS DEAD THAN IT WAS WHEN I WAS ALIVE!

NORNS BE WITH ME! WHEREVER YOU ARE!

I'D SAY THIS IS THE END FOR US, BROTHER. LET'S MAKE A GOOD BLOODY SHOW OF IT.

AYE, TYR, AND I SUPPOSE IF WE'VE GOT ANY LAST WORDS...PERHAPS IN THE WAY OF APOLOGY FOR PAST BEATINGS OF OUR KIN...NOW WOULD BE THE TIME TO UTTER THEM?

NOTHING COMES TO MIND.

I FIGURED.

KRAKAKOOM!!

"...PREPARE TO BE BLUDGEONED MOST SEVERELY!"

HA. NEVER THOUGHT THAT SOUND WOULD MAKE ME SMILE.

PREPARE TO KNOW WHAT IT'S LIKE TO BE ME, SONS OF MUSPEL! IN OTHER WORDS...

WARRIORS OF THE DUSK LANDS! WHEN YOU FELL VALIANTLY IN BATTLE, YOU THOUGHT THIS AFTERLIFE WOULD BE YOUR ETERNAL REWARD!

AND SO IT IS! FOR NOW THE SON OF ODIN HAS COME UNTO YOU BEARING THE GREATEST GIFT IN ALL THE HEAVENS!

STAY DOWN, SINDR--

--OR JOIN YOUR FATHER IN OBLIVION.

SPEAK ANOTHER WORD OF MY FATHER, AND I SWEAR BY THE FIRES OF MUSPELHEIM, I WILL SEE YOUR ENTIRE FAMILY BURNED TO ASH, ODINSON!

TO HEL WITH YOUR FATHER.

AND IF YOU'VE A QUARREL WITH MY FAMILY...

...WE CAN SETTLE IT NOW.

KEEP YOUR PATHETIC LAND OF THE DEAD. BY THE TIME I'M DONE WITH YOU LOT...YOU'LL ALL BELONG HERE FOREVER!

MALEKITH! USE YOUR BLACK BIFROST TO GET ME OUT OF HERE!

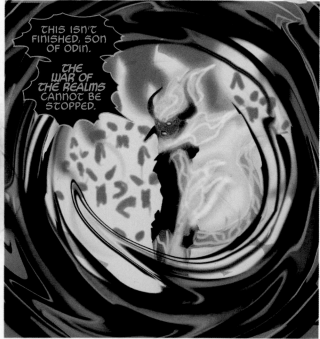

THIS ISN'T FINISHED, SON OF ODIN.

THE WAR OF THE REALMS CANNOT BE STOPPED.

AND SO ENDED ONE GREAT BATTLE IN HEL....AS ANOTHER THREATENED TO BEGIN.

WE GO AFTER THEM-- INTO THE FIRES OF MUSPELHEIM IF WE HAVE TO!

AND THEN WE MARCH ON *SVARTALFHEIM*, RIGHT TO MALEKITH'S DOORSTEP, AND END THIS WAR ONCE AND FOR--

NO! GIVE ME BACK MY CROWN!

NOW THE *REAL* WAR BEGINS. THE ONE FOR MY *THRONE*. UNLESS YOU'RE FINALLY READY TO BEND THE KNEE, BALDER.

WE HAD A DEAL, HELA.

PERHAPS WE DID, BUT YOU NEVER SAID YOUR VOWS. THE *MARRIAGE* WAS NEVER SEALED.

BECAUSE WE FOUGHT A FLAMING WAR TO SAVE YOUR REALM FROM BEING CONQUERED AND BURNED! WOULD YOU TRULY PLUNGE IT RIGHT BACK INTO CARNAGE?!

I WOULD SEE MYSELF WHERE I *BELONG*, BACK ON THE THRONE OF--

I DO!

I NOW PRONOUNCE YOU...AH... ...QUEENS OF HEL.

CONGRATULATIONS, DEAR WIFE. GOOD LUCK SURVIVING THE HONEYMOON.

YOU CAN KEEP YOUR LUCK, HELA. I PREFER A GOOD SWORD.

AS LOKI'S MAGIC AND KARNILLA'S SACRIFICE RETURNED US TO THE LAND OF THE LIVING, I WANTED TO BELIEVE I WAS LEAVING HEL IN BETTER SHAPE THAN I FOUND IT.

BUT THERE WERE STILL PRICES TO BE PAID FOR WHAT WE'D DONE.

WE WERE PROMISED AN ODINSON. I SUPPOSE YOU'LL DO.

HA! SPLENDID! WHAT TIME IS THE FEAST?

WHENEVER YOU'RE DONE PREPARING IT, TYR. NOW GET TO THE KITCHEN AND FIND AN APRON. I HOPE YOU'RE BETTER AT COOKING THAN YOU ARE AT GROWING BEARDS.

AND STILL MORE WARS TO BE FOUGHT.

WELL, SINDR, IF THE LEGIONS OF THE DEAD ARE TOO MUCH FOR YOU...LET'S HOPE YOU'RE BETTER AT SLAUGHTERING THE LIVING.

BUT FOR A MOMENT AT LEAST, THERE WAS A TIME TO RAISE A TOAST TO VICTORY. AND REUNIONS.

*FEEL STRANGE AT ALL?

MIDGARD.
NEWARK HARBOR.

BEING *ALIVE* AGAIN?

FEELS... COMPLICATED.

I'M STILL NOT SURE HOW KARNILLA DID IT. ALL I KNOW IS THAT... I CANNOT SQUANDER THE LIFE I'VE BEEN GIVEN. EVEN IF MY HEART BELONGS IN HEL.

IF NOTHING ELSE, IT WILL BE NICE TO SEE *MOTHER* AGAIN.

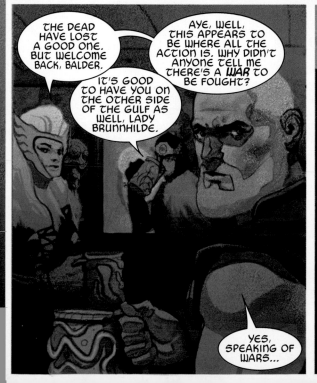

THE DEAD HAVE LOST A GOOD ONE. BUT WELCOME BACK, BALDER.

IT'S GOOD TO HAVE YOU ON THE OTHER SIDE OF THE GULF AS WELL, LADY BRUNNHILDE.

AYE, WELL, THIS APPEARS TO BE WHERE ALL THE ACTION IS. WHY DIDN'T ANYONE TELL ME THERE'S A *WAR* TO BE FOUGHT?

YES, SPEAKING OF WARS...

I DID MY PART, BROTHER. I SAID I'D SEND YOU INTO THE REALMS TO HELP THWART MALEKITH'S PLAN. AND SO I DID.

WE WON A BATTLE, LOKI. BUT THE WAR STILL RAGES.

NEVERTHELESS, I WILL CLAIM MY *PRICE* NOW, AS WE AGREED.

I NEVER AGREED TO ANYTHING. YOU SAID YOU SOUGHT SOMETHING I HAVE ON THIS BOAT, BUT IF YOU THINK FOR ONE SECOND I'M GOING TO LET YOU WALK OUT OF HERE WITH A WEAPON OF POWER, YOU ARE--

5

OLD GODS

"BEST *BAR* I EVER BEEN TO, *HUH?* ON EARTH, OR ANYWHERE?"

LET US STICK TO MIDGARD FOR NOW.

SURE. ALL RIGHT.

THERE WAS THIS LITTLE PLACE ON *SAIPAN* IN '44.

DON'T KNOW THE NAME. IF IT HAD ONE, IT'D BEEN BLASTED OFF BY THEN. AFTER A MONTH OF FIGHTING, THE PLACE WAS BARELY STANDING. SO WAS I.

I STUMBLED IN THERE AFTER WE'D FINALLY TAKEN THE ISLAND. *SAKE* TASTED SWEETER THAN ANYTHING THAT HAD TOUCHED MY LIPS IN YEARS.

TRIED TO HAVE A SHOT FOR EVERY JAPANESE CORPSE I'D PUT IN THAT GROUND. PASSED OUT BEFORE I MADE IT HALFWAY THROUGH...

A FINE CHOICE, *LOGAN.* RATHER *MOROSE,* BUT A FINE CHOICE INDEED.

MINE WOULD BE THE LONGHOUSE OF THE VIKING CHIEFTAIN *ULFAR THE BLOODBEARD.*

A HOVEL ON THE MUDDY SHORES OF *ICELAND* THAT WAS ALWAYS PACKED TO THE RAFTERS WITH BLOOD-DRENCHED NORSEMEN STINKING OF FISH AND GOATS STINKING OF... *GOAT.*

BUT ULFAR BREWED THE FINEST MEAD IN ALL THE LAND. AND FATHERED THE FINEST DAUGHTERS.

EVEN NOW THE SMELL OF GOAT BRINGS A TEAR TO MY EYE AND A STIRRING TO MY LOINS...

DEFINITELY DIDN'T NEED TO KNOW THAT LAST PART. GONNA POP SOME CLAWS IN MY BRAIN NOW.

I SAY THEE NAY! RAISE YOUR GLASS, *WOLVERINE!*

...YOU WILL BE DAMNED, WOLVERINE!
DAMNED TO ALL THE HELS THAT KING THOR CAN MUSTER!
BRING IT ON, BUB! IT'S WAY PAST TIME SOMEBODY CARVED SOME OF THE EGO OFF YOU!
AND OLD MAN PHOENIX IS JUST THE FLAMING BASTARD TO DO IT!
THUNDER RUMBLES AND COSMIC FIRE ROARS. ANCIENT POWERS ARE UNLEASHED ON A COLOSSALLY DESTRUCTIVE SCALE.
YET ALL AROUND THESE TWO WARRING GODS, THE UNIVERSE MERELY SHRUGS.
AND GOES ON WITH ITS DYING.

INTERLUDE.
ELSEWHERE AT
THE END OF TIME.

THE LAST POD OF *ACANTI WHALES* LEFT IN ALL THE COSMOS HAVE BEEN SWIMMING FOR LIGHT-YEARS, STARVING AND SINGING THEIR DEATH SONG...

...WHILE SEARCHING THE DESOLATE REACHES OF SPACE FOR A STAR TO HURL THEMSELVES INTO, AS IS THEIR WAY.

BUT OUT HERE THERE ARE NO STARS. ONLY DARKNESS.

A DARKNESS THAT *HUNGERS.*

THE LIVING DARKNESS OF *EGO THE NECROWORLD.*

JOIN *GALACTUS* IN MY MOLTEN GULLET, LITTLE FISHES! GALACTUS AND THE ARMADAS OF THE *KREE'AR EMPIRE* AND THE LAST OF THOSE FUMBLING, INBRED *CELESTIALS!*

NOTHING THAT LIVES IN ALL THE HEAVENS CAN STAND BEFORE EGO!

ONCE, THERE HAD BEEN A SWORD CALLED *ALL-BLACK.*

ALL-BLACK THE NECROSWORD. THE SHADOW BLADE FORGED BY KNULL, GOD OF THE SYMBIOTES, THAT BECAME THE INFERNAL WEAPON OF GORR THE GOD BUTCHER.

THE BLADE THAT SLEW A BILLION GODS. AND NOW THAT SAME DARK POWER SLITHERS THROUGH THE VOLCANIC VEINS OF EGO.

A LIVING PLANET DRIVEN MAD AND MADE OF MURDER. THE STRONGEST FORCE IN A DYING UNIVERSE.

OR SO IT WOULD SEEM.

I CAN STAND BEFORE YOU.

WHAT? WHO SAID THAT?

I DID. DOWN HERE. CRAWLING ON YOUR SURFACE.

I CHALLENGE YOU, MIGHTY EGO, TO A ROUND OF COMBAT.

A BATTLE TO THE DEATH.

HA HA HA HA! I HAVE BEEN CHALLENGED BY A WORM! WHAT MADNESS IS THIS?

I WILL ALLOW YOU ONE CHANCE TO YIELD PEACEFULLY, IF YOU SO DESIRE.

GIVE ME THE POWER OF THE NECROSWORD, AND I PROMISE NOT TO HURT YOU.

HURT ME? YOU ARE AN IMPUDENT LITTLE WORM, AREN'T YOU?

VERY WELL, IF IT'S DEATH YOU SO DESIRE...

THE CYCLONE IS THE SIZE OF A SUPERNOVA, SUCKING UP CHUNKS OF DEAD WORLDS FROM PARSECS AWAY.

AND TURNING THEM INTO LIGHTNING-CHARGED COMETS.

IT HAS BEEN YEARS SINCE ALL-FATHER THOR ERUPTED WITH SO MUCH GODLY POWER. IT'S ALMOST ENOUGH TO MAKE HIM SMILE.

ALMOST.

THE PHOENIX RAPTOR STRETCHES FOR LIGHT-YEARS. A FIREBIRD THE SIZE OF A GALAXY. HIS CLAWS BURN HOT ENOUGH TO MELT STARS.

NO LONGER IS HE LOGAN OR EVEN THE PHOENIX. HE IS BECOME A THING MADE SOLELY OF RAGE AND FIRE.

THE COSMIC BERSERKER.

RRRRRRGGGHHH!!!

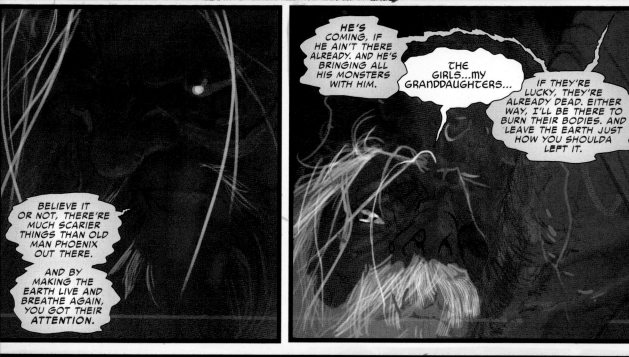

BELIEVE IT OR NOT, THERE'RE MUCH SCARIER THINGS THAN OLD MAN PHOENIX OUT THERE.

AND BY MAKING THE EARTH LIVE AND BREATHE AGAIN, YOU GOT THEIR ATTENTION.

HE'S COMING, IF HE AIN'T THERE ALREADY. AND HE'S BRINGING ALL HIS MONSTERS WITH HIM.

THE GIRLS...MY GRANDDAUGHTERS...

IF THEY'RE LUCKY, THEY'RE ALREADY DEAD. EITHER WAY, I'LL BE THERE TO BURN THEIR BODIES. AND LEAVE THE EARTH JUST HOW YOU SHOULDA LEFT IT.

DEAD AND GONE.

ADIOS, ALL-FATHER.

HE IS THE FIST OF IRON!
THE STARBRAND SUPREME!
THE MASTER OF MYSTIC VENGEANCE!
HE IS DOOM!
KNEEL BEFORE HIS OMNIPOTENCE AND DESPAIR!

6

MIDGARD'S FINAL DOOM

WHAT IS THAT THING? I'VE NEVER SEEN ANYTHING LIKE IT.

ADAM, I'M FRIGHTENED.

DON'T BE SCARED, MY LOVE. OUR GOD WILL WATCH OVER US, AS ALWAYS. JUST TRUST IN HIM.

TRUST IN THE MIGHTY THOR.

BUT WHERE IS--

AAAGHH!!!

HERE.

IT WAS RIGHT HERE.

WHAT IN THE NAME OF DOOM HAVE YOU DONE TO IT?

ONCE THERE WAS A CHALLENGE BETWEEN A **WORM** AND A **WORLD.** A BATTLE TO THE DEATH.

IT DID NOT GO AS ONE MIGHT EXPECT.

≠HUFF≠
≠HUFF≠

STILL HERE.

CURSE YOU, WORM.

YOU'RE SO...SMALL AND WORTHLESS...I'M TEARING MYSELF **APART** TO TRY TO KILL YOU.

SO YOU GIVE UP, THEN?

IT DOES NOT MATTER. THERE'S STILL NO POSSIBLE WAY YOU COULD EVER HARM **EGO THE NECROWORLD.**

NOT IN A MILLION YEARS!

OH, IT WON'T TAKE NEARLY THAT LONG.

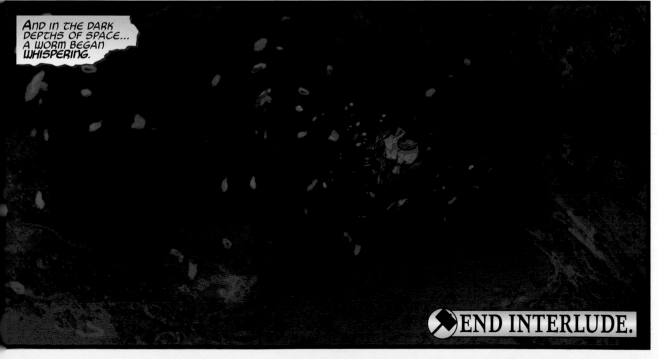

AND IN THE DARK DEPTHS OF SPACE... A WORM BEGAN **WHISPERING.**

✕ **END INTERLUDE.**

YOU'RE NOT GOD ENOUGH TO HOLD THIS HAMMER!
AND SO THE FIREBIRD WAS REBORN YET AGAIN, WITH A HEART OF LIGHTNING AND A FISTFUL OF BURNING URU.
AS THE MIGHTY THUNDERBIRD.
KING PHOENIX, GOD OF FIRE.
BUT IF YOU'RE LOOKING TO PLAY THE DEVIL, THOR WILL OBLIGE!
AND THE WORLD SHOOK FROM WITHIN, AS THE GREATEST GOD AND THE GREATEST DEVIL EXPLODED WITH ALL THE FIRE LEFT IN CREATION.

DAY TURNED TO NIGHT AND NIGHT TURNED TO DAY, AND STILL THE BATTLE RAGED WITHIN THE EARTH.

FOR MANY YEARS TO COME, THERE WOULD BE FIERY EARTHQUAKES AND VOLCANOES THAT SPEWED LIGHTNING AND ROARS LOUD ENOUGH TO CRUMBLE MOUNTAINS.

BUT LIFE WOULD ENDURE.

GENERATIONS WOULD COME AND GO, NEVER KNOWING A WORLD THAT WASN'T ROARING AND CRACKING APART.

NEVER KNOWING A NIGHT WITHOUT SCREAMS FROM DEEP BELOW.

THE GARDENS WERE TENDED. THE STARS STAYED LIT. WHILE THE UNIVERSE CREPT CLOSER TO ITS END.

EVEN DEEP WITHIN THE EARTH, THOR COULD FEEL IT.

THE EARTH CLINGING TO LIFE, AT THE END OF TIME.

HE CLUNG TO THAT LIFE TOO. AND THE WORLD...

...BECAME THOR'S MIGHTIEST HAMMER.

"DO YOU *FEEL* THAT?"

I FEEL NOTHING.

EXACTLY. THE GROUND STOPPED SHAKING.

THAT'S IMPOSSIBLE. THE OLD ONES SAY THE GROUND HAS ALWAYS BEEN SHAKING. WHAT DOES IT MEAN?

IT...IT MEANS...

IT MEANS GOD IS GOOD.

IT IS FINISHED.

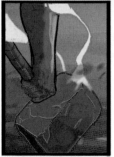

THOR?! HE'S RETURNED TO US!

DAUGHTER, RUN! GET THE ELDERS! QUICKLY!

DAUGHTER? WHAT'S HAPPENED TO YOUR...

IT'S TOO LATE, MOMMIES. GOD IS SLEEPING THE *FOREVER SLEEP* NOW. A LITTLE BIRD TOLD ME.

AND THE *REAL DARKNESS* IS AWAKE AGAIN.

"AND NOW IT'S COMING FOR US ALL."

7

YOUNG THOR'S LAMENT

AAAARRGGHHH!!!

EEEEIIIIGGHHH!!!

YAAAGGHHH!!!

I REALIZED... THAT MY ALL-FATHER WAS *NOT* MY EVERYTHING.

EVEN AT A YOUNG AGE, I BEGAN TO LEARN LESSONS MY FATHER COULD NEVER TEACH ME.

I LEARNED OF JOY AND PASSION AND THE THIRST FOR ADVENTURE. AND WHAT IT TRULY MEANT TO BE YOUNG, ALIVE AND IMMORTAL.

THAT IS HOW AN ALL-FATHER METES OUT JUSTICE. WITH HIS OWN TWO OMNIPOTENT HANDS.

DO YOU SEE, *THOR?* SOMEDAY THIS WILL BE YOUR...

BUT I DID NOT LEARN THESE LESSONS IN ASGARD.

I ONLY LEARNED WHAT I LOVED ABOUT BEING A GOD...

THOR?

WHERE IN THE HEL *IS* THAT BOY?!

...ONCE I WAS AMONG THE MORTALS.

THE WINDS WERE ROARING AT OUR BACKS TODAY! AND THE WAVES FOAMED RED WITH THE BLOOD OF OUR ENEMIES!

ALL THANKS TO THE GOD OF THUNDER!

ALL THANKS TO THOR!

TO THOR!

TO THOR!

RAISE THOSE HORNS TO YOURSELVES AS WELL, MEN OF THE SNOWLAND. FOR THE LONGHOUSE OF ULFAR THE BLOODBEARD IS HOME TO THE FINEST VIKINGS IN ALL OF MIDGARD.

AND 'TIS YOUR GOD WHO SHOULD BE THANKING YOU.

IN ASGARD, THEY SAY THOR IS WILD AND BRASH. AND AYE, PERHAPS THEY ARE RIGHT.

BUT I TELL YOU THIS: AMONG YOU PEOPLE, THOR HAS LEARNED SOMETHING THAT HAS ELUDED EVEN THE WISEST ASGARDIANS.

A GOD IS ONLY AS MIGHTY AS HIS WORSHIPERS.

SO WHEN I LOOK AROUND AT YOU BRINY, BLOOD-DRENCHED BASTARDS, I KNOW WHY THOR IS THE MIGHTIEST GOD WHO EVER--

RRRWK

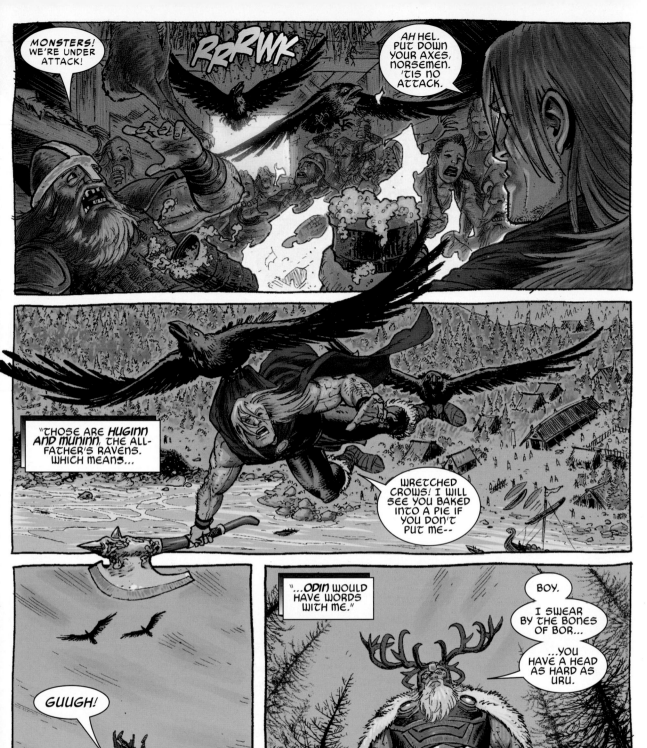

FUNNY. I OFTEN SAY THE SAME ABOUT *YOU*, FATHER.

MIND YOUR IMPUDENT TONGUE OR I'LL HAVE THE BIRDS MIND IT FOR YOU! I AM SICK OF BEING DEFIED BY MY OWN FLESH AND BLOOD!

HOW MANY TIMES HAVE I TOLD YOU TO STAY AWAY FROM MIDGARD?!

AM I MEANT TO ANSWER THAT? OR KEEP MINDING MY IMPUDENT TONGUE?

YOU ARROGANT LITTLE BASTARD!

GUUGH!

YOU GO TOO FAR, THOR! I HAVE LAID ENTIRE *WORLDS* TO RUIN FOR GIVING LESS OFFENSE THAN YOU HURL AT ME ON A DAILY BASIS!

I'LL REMIND YOU THAT I WAS MINDING MY OWN DAMN BUSINESS UNTIL YOUR RAVENS DRAGGED ME HERE. I'LL GLADLY RETURN TO MY MEAD.

LOOK AT YOURSELF! YOU DO NOT *BELONG* HERE, BOY!

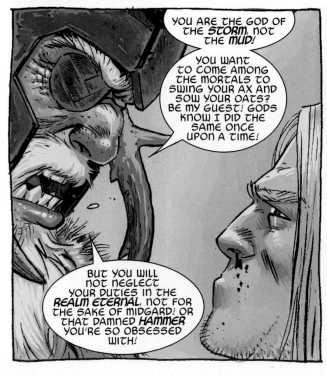

YOU ARE THE GOD OF THE *STORM*, NOT THE *MUD!*

YOU WANT TO COME AMONG THE MORTALS TO SWING YOUR AX AND SOW YOUR OATS? BE MY GUEST! GODS KNOW I DID THE SAME ONCE UPON A TIME!

BUT YOU WILL NOT NEGLECT YOUR DUTIES IN THE *REALM ETERNAL*, NOT FOR THE SAKE OF MIDGARD! OR THAT DAMNED *HAMMER* YOU'RE SO OBSESSED WITH!

YOU UNDERSTAND *NOTHING* OF MIDGARD. OR OF ME. *OLD MAN.*

IF YOU WANT GODS BLINDLY *KOWTOWING* AT YOUR FEET, THEN GO BACK TO ASGARD.

AND LEAVE ME HERE IN THE *MUD* WHERE I BELONG.

"I HAVE SLAIN ARMIES OF FLAMING GIANTS AND TOWERING MONSTERS FROM BEYOND THE STARS..."

...BUT IT'S MY OWN *SON* WHO WILL BE THE DEATH OF ME. THIS I KNOW.

PERHAPS.

OR PERHAPS IT'S YOUR SON WHO'LL SAVE THE DAY.

BE GONE, *LOKI*. I'M OF NO MIND TO DEAL WITH YOUR FOUL MISCHIEF.

BE YE CERTAIN OF THAT, SIRE? FOR IT APPEARS THAT A BIT OF MY MISCHIEF IS EXACTLY WHAT YOU NEED TO SOLVE YOUR PESKY...*THOR PROBLEM.*

LOKI, I WARN YOU...

I HATE TO SEE THE WAY HE TREATS YOU, FATHER. WITH SUCH BLATANT DISRESPECT. SPURNING THE ALMIGHTY ALL-FATHER IN FAVOR OF A FEW LOWLY MORTALS.

MY POOR LOST BROTHER MUST BE MADE TO SEE THE ERROR OF HIS WAYS. AND I CAN DO THAT. IF YOU BUT GIVE ME *FREE REIN,* I PROMISE YOU, MY LIEGE...

...I CAN MAKE IT SO THOR *NEVER* WISHES TO SEE MIDGARD AGAIN.

YOUR PLAN ISN'T WORKING, LOKI.

HE DOESN'T APPEAR TO BE WINNING HER FAVOR.

YES, WELL, MY BROTHER IS NOT EXACTLY HERCULES WHEN IT COMES TO THE ART OF WOOING. I SUPPOSE WE'LL HAVE TO GIVE THE POOR FOOL A BIT OF HELP.

AH, GREETINGS. PERHAPS WE SHOULD START AGAIN. I AM THOR, SON OF ODIN. AND AH, YOU ARE VERY GOOD AT SLAYING. DO YOU SLAY HERE OFTEN OR...

GRAGH, WAS I NOT CLEAR? HOP ON YOUR RAINBOW BRIDGE AND TAKE YOUR PRETTY-BOY ASS BACK TO ASGARD! I DON'T NEED ANY HELP FROM THE GODS WHEN IT COMES TO--

RRRRGGGHH!!!

ARRRGGH! A ROCK TROLL!

HELLO, CRUNCHY LITTLE MEAT SNACKS!

FALL BACK! WE'LL SURROUND IT WITH--

RELAX, MORTALS. LEAVE THIS ONE TO THE PRETTY BOY.

HAVE AT THEE, TROLL!

"...IT'S WORKING TO PERFECTION."

I SHOWED ERIKA THE WORLD FROM THE BACK OF A FLYING GOAT, AND SAW IT ALL ANEW THROUGH HER EYES.

SHE SHOWED ME THAT BEING **IMMORTAL** DIDN'T MEAN ANYTHING...IF YOU COULDN'T LEARN TO APPRECIATE EACH AND EVERY **DAY**.

SHE DID. NEVER HAD I SEEN A MORTAL WHO SO LIVED LIFE TO ITS FULLEST.

SHE NEVER ASKED ABOUT ASGARD. OR VALHALLA.

SHE TREATED ME NOT LIKE A GOD, BUT LIKE A **MAN**.

EXCEPT THE ONCE.

EVERY TIME THERE'S A *RAVEN* AROUND... I SEE YOU FLINCH.

HHR. DO I?

AYE, YOU DO.

'TIS NOTHING.

HE DOESN'T LIKE IT THAT YOU'RE HERE, DOES HE?

HE...DOESN'T UNDERSTAND THIS PLACE.

PERHAPS HE UNDERSTANDS MORE THAN YOU THINK.

IN MY EXPERIENCE, *FATHERS* ARE ONLY GOOD FOR ONE THING--GIVING US SOMETHING TO *RISE* ABOVE.

THAT'S *EXACTLY* WHAT YOU WILL DO. AND ODIN *KNOWS* IT.

NEVER BE ASHAMED OF THAT, MY LOVE.

OR OF *US.*

I...I THINK I *LOVE* YOU, ERIKA OF MIDGARD.

SHOW ME.

"*LOKI! YOU UTTER FOOL! WHAT HAVE YOU DONE?*"

ALL I EVER DO IS SERVE YOU, YOUR HOLINESS. HOW MAY LOKI SERVE YOU NOW?

YOU'VE DONE ENOUGH! I SHOULD'VE KNOWN YOU'D ONLY MAKE EVERYTHING *WORSE!*

MY LORD, I DON'T--

YOU'VE MADE IT SO THOR SPENDS MORE TIME ON MIDGARD THAN EVER! HE NEVER LEAVES THOSE CURSED SHORES OR THAT BLASTED MORTAL WOMAN'S SIDE!

THAT WAS YOUR PLAN ALL ALONG, WASN'T IT, YOU LYING--

NAY, MY LORD!

THE PLAN ISN'T *FINISHED.* NOW COMES THE *BEST* PART.

NO MORE, LOKI. NO MORE WILL I LET YOU TAMPER WITH THE THREADS OF FATE.

AH, BUT THIS IS ONLY A *MINOR* TAMPERING, MY LORD, I ASSURE YOU.

JUST ONE LITTLE *WAR.* THAT'S ALL WE NEED.

IT WAS THEN THAT THE DARK ELVES WENT TO WAR WITH THE DWARVES, A RECURRING CONFLICT SEEMINGLY AS OLD AS WAR ITSELF.

AND AS ALWAYS, THE GODS OF ASGARD WERE COMPELLED TO INTERVENE.

SO ONE MORNING I LEFT THE SIDE OF ERIKA THE RED. FOR THE GOOD OF THE REALMS.

WHATEVER WORDS WE SHARED THAT DAY I AM ASHAMED TO SAY HAVE BEEN LOST TO THE ANNALS OF TIME.

I JUST KNOW I PROMISED HER I WOULD RETURN AS SOON AS THE FIGHTING HAD FINISHED.

AND SO I DID.

THE VILLAGE HAS CHANGED.

ERIKA! YOUR THOR HAS RETURNED! ERIKA THE RED!

SHE ISN'T HERE.

BUT I CAN TAKE YOU TO HER.

SHE *WAITED* FOR YOU.

EVERY DAY, STANDING ON THIS SPOT, LOOKING OUT AT THE HORIZON.

SEEMED RIGHT TO *BURY* HER HERE.

NO...

WHO WAS IT? TROLLS? RAIDERS? WHO COULD POSSIBLY HAVE *KILLED* HER? AND WHERE DO I *FIND* THEM?

NO ONE KILLED HER. SHE LIVED A LONG AND FULL LIFE, MUCH LONGER THAN MOST. I THINK IT WAS HER YEARNING TO SEE YOU AGAIN THAT KEPT HER GOING SO LONG.

SO LONG...? I DON'T UNDERSTAND. I...I WAS ONLY GONE...

FORTY YEARS.

SHE WAITED 40 YEARS. AND DIED BUT THREE DAYS AGO.

BEFORE SHE WENT, SHE ASKED ME TO GIVE YOU A MESSAGE.

"SHOW ME," SHE SAID.

I HOPE THAT HAS SOME MEANING TO YOU, MY LORD.

HAAAA HA HA HAA HA!

AND *NOW*, DEAR FATHER, NOW THAT LOKI HAS FULFILLED WHAT HE PROMISED...IT'S TIME TO DISCUSS WHAT I EXPECT IN *RETURN*.

A *TRIFLE*, REALLY. I'M SURE IT'LL HARDLY BE MISSED...

LOKI!

AH YES, FATHER, I WAS JUST ABOUT TO--

HE'S STILL THERE!

WHAT?

HGGHK!

THOR IS STILL ON MIDGARD!

IMPOSSIBLE.

WHY WOULD HE STILL BE THERE? AFTER WHAT HE LOST, WHY WOULD HE EVER--GAGGH!

THIS IS MY FAULT FOR LISTENING TO YOU. NOW WE DO THIS *MY* WAY.

WHERE'S MY *SPEAR?*

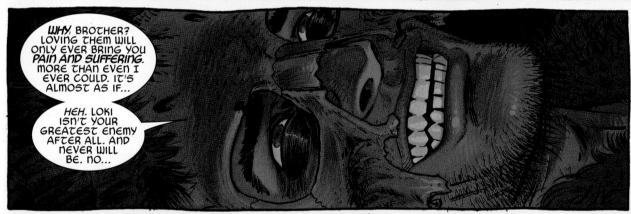

WHY, BROTHER? LOVING THEM WILL ONLY EVER BRING YOU *PAIN AND SUFFERING.* MORE THAN EVEN I EVER COULD. IT'S ALMOST AS IF...

HEH. LOKI ISN'T YOUR GREATEST ENEMY AFTER ALL. AND NEVER WILL BE. NO...

"...IT'S *MIDGARD.*"

I NEVER THOUGHT ABOUT TURNING MY BACK ON THE REALM I LOVED. THAT WOULD HAVE BEEN THE SAME AS LETTING HER GO. LETTING HER DIE IN VAIN.

AND THAT, I WILL *NEVER* DO.

LEND ME YOUR EARS AND YOUR MEAD, MEN OF THE NORTH!

8

PRISON OF ANGELS

YESTERDAY. MANHATTAN.

KRAKOOM!

HE'S *SURLY* TODAY.

I CAN TELL BY THE *THUNDER*. THE *WAR* MUST BE GETTING TO HIM.

GRRRR, STUPID SKY DROOL.

SKY DROOL NOT GOOD FOR LADY MASTER. *JANE AND THORI* WALK *FASTER* NOW.

RELAX, THORI. A LITTLE STORM'S NOT GONNA KILL ME.

GOD, I WISH I WAS UP THERE IN IT.

NOTHING WILL KILL LADY MASTER WHILE THORI WALKING HER!

JANE AND THORI MURDER *CANCER* NOW! *MURDER MURDER MURDER!*

YOU'RE A GOOD DOG, THORI, BUT NOT SO LOUD WITH THE MURDERS.

THORI SORRY.

MURDER MURDER MURDER!

THE DAY BEFORE YESTERDAY. AVENGERS MOUNTAIN.

"UGH, IT SMELLS LIKE GOAT IN HERE."

LET ME GUESS, THOR JUST LEFT.

IN A BIT OF A HUFF, YES.

HE HAVE A BAD DATE WITH THE HULK? UH, HE'S TOTALLY DATING THE HULK NOW, YOU KNOW THAT, RIGHT, MR. CHAIRMAN?

JEALOUSY DOES NOT BECOME YOU, TONY STARK. AND NO, THOR'S FLEDGLING RELATIONSHIP WITH MS. WALTERS IS NOT THE ISSUE.

IT'S HIS BROTHER.

STILL NO SIGN OF LOKI, HUH?

TOO MANY SIGNS. AFTER WE LAST SAW HIM IN THE HANDS OF THE CELESTIALS,* HE SOMEHOW BECAME INVOLVED IN THE BATTLE FOR THE INFINITY STONES.** SINCE THEN WE'VE LOST TRACK OF HIM AGAIN.

HE'S BEEN A VERY BUSY GOD LATELY. AND AFTER HIS WHOLE EMO ANTI-HERO PHASE, IT DEFINITELY LOOKS LIKE HE'S BACK TO HIS OLD SUPER EVIL SELF AGAIN, HUH?

PERHAPS.

HE DID BRING THE AVENGERS BACK TOGETHER.

YEAH, BY TRYING TO DESTROY THE WORLD WITH KILLER SPACE GIANTS!

STILL, I BELIEVE THAT FROM LOKI'S WARPED PERSPECTIVE, THIS HAS ALL BEEN ABOUT HELPING US. TO BE READY.

READY FOR WHAT, T'CHALLA?

FOR WAR. TELL ME, IRON MAN...

*SEE AVENGERS (2018) #1-6!

**SEE INFINITY WARS (2018) #1-6!

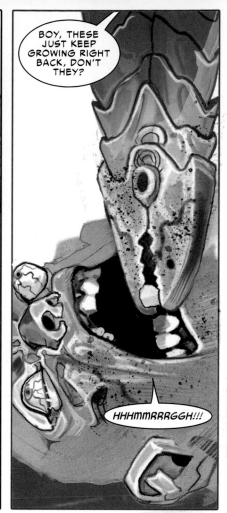

DID THEY **KILL** YOU YET?

GO AWAY... ANGELS. THOR HAS NOTHING... TO CONFESS. YET.

IF YOU'RE TRYING TO CALL YOUR HAMMER, DON'T BOTHER. IT WON'T BE ABLE TO REACH YOU.

YOUR WEAPONS ARE LOST INSIDE A MINIATURIZED **BLACK HOLE.** THEIR VERSION OF SOLITARY CONFINEMENT.

YOU... IS... IS IT **REALLY** YOU?

SISTER?

THIS PRISON IS THE SIZE OF A PLANET AND, AS NEAR AS I CAN TELL, **EMPTY** EXCEPT FOR US.

YET THEY PUT US IN CELLS SIDE BY SIDE? WHY WOULD THEY DO THAT?

IF YOU KNEW HEVEN LIKE I DO, BROTHER, IT'D BE OBVIOUS.

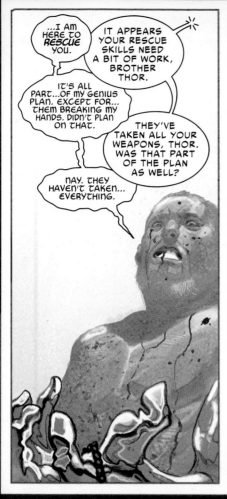

...I AM HERE TO **RESCUE** YOU.

IT APPEARS YOUR RESCUE SKILLS NEED A BIT OF WORK, BROTHER THOR.

IT'S ALL PART...OF MY **GENIUS** PLAN. EXCEPT FOR... THEM BREAKING MY HANDS. DIDN'T PLAN ON THAT.

THEY'VE TAKEN ALL YOUR WEAPONS, THOR. WAS THAT PART OF THE PLAN AS WELL?

NAY. THEY HAVEN'T TAKEN... EVERYTHING.

MJOLNIR.

THEY DIDN'T TAKE... MY MJOLNIR.

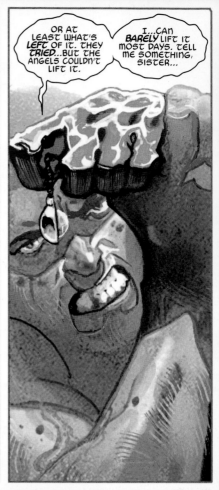

OR AT LEAST WHAT'S **LEFT** OF IT. THEY **TRIED**...BUT THE ANGELS COULDN'T LIFT IT.

I...CAN **BARELY** LIFT IT MOST DAYS. TELL ME SOMETHING, SISTER...

AM I **WORTHY?**

ASK ME THAT QUESTION AGAIN ONCE WE'RE FREE OF THIS PLACE, THOR.

I DO HOPE THERE'S MORE TO THIS ESCAPE PLAN OF YOURS.

YES, THERE'S...

GAGGGHH!!!

...BUT DO YOU SUPPOSE WE COULD SKIP TO THE PART WHERE WE BREAK THE HEL *OUT* OF HERE?

VALKYRIE? I FIGURED THIS WAS YOUR IDEA.

YOU DIDN'T THINK I'D MISS A CHANCE TO PUNCH ANGELS, DID YOU? STILL WAITING ON THAT. INSTEAD I'M DODGING BLADES.

WAR IS RAGING. DIDN'T KNOW WHAT SIDE YOUR *ADOPTED REALM* WOULD FALL ON, ANGELA. UNTIL BRUNNHILDE HERE TOLD ME YOU'D DISAPPEARED, AND TOGETHER WE CAME SEARCHING.

SO IT'S TRUE THEN, HEVEN HAS SIDED WITH *MALEKITH?*

I'M AFRAID SO.

THEN *AYE,* LADIES...

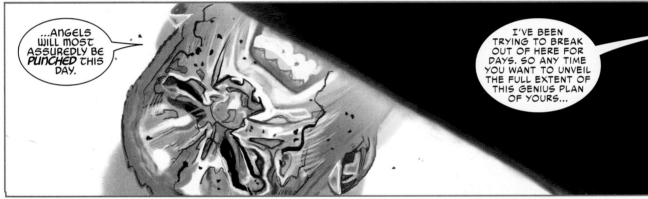

...ANGELS WILL MOST ASSUREDLY BE *PUNCHED* THIS DAY.

I'VE BEEN TRYING TO BREAK OUT OF HERE FOR DAYS. SO ANY TIME YOU WANT TO UNVEIL THE FULL EXTENT OF THIS GENIUS PLAN OF YOURS...

THE GOD OF THUNDER IS NO FOOL, SISTER. WE DID NOT COME HERE ALONE. BRUNNHILDE AND I BROUGHT *BACKUP.*

SPLENDID. WHO IS IT? PLEASE SAY SKURGE AND THE DESTROYER AND THE REST OF THE ASGARDIANS OF THE GALAXY.

MY *GOAT.*

AND MY *DOG.*

ALSO VALKYRIE'S *HORSE.*

MY FAMILY IS INSANE.

THERE ARE HUNDREDS OF BATTLE-HARDENED ANGELIC WARRIORS ONBOARD THIS SHIP.

I HATE TO BREAK IT TO YOU, GOD OF THUNDER, BUT YOUR PRECIOUS ANIMALS ARE MOST ASSUREDLY ALREADY *DEAD.* SO I SUGGEST WE--

THOOGOM

THORI SORRY WE LATE. THORI LOSE TRACK OF TIME WHEN *MURDERING*.

MASTER READY TO *GO* NOW?

AYE, ALMOST, DOG. JUST WAITING ON...ONE LAST THING...

THE GRAVITY WELL IS COMING APART AT THE SEAMS!

SOMETHING JUST CAME FLYING OUT OF IT!

THAT'S *IMPOSSIBLE!* WHAT IN THE NAME OF *HEVEN* WAS *IN* THERE?

THERE WAS ONLY ONE *MJOLNIR*, BUT 'TIS NOT ALWAYS THE *HAMMER* THAT IS MOST IMPORTANT...

HE SLEEPS ONLY WHEN EXHAUSTION COMES OVER HIM LIKE A FEVER. I'VE SEEN HIM EAT BUT ONCE IN THE LAST MONTH, AND HE DID SO WITH A LOOK OF PROFOUND SHAME.

IF HE ISN'T OFF SAVING THE WORLD WITH HIS AVENGERS, HE IS SEARCHING TIRELESSLY DAY AND NIGHT FOR A WAY TO ACCESS THE OTHER REALMS. AT THE RATE HE IS GOING...

...I'M WORRIED THAT THOR WILL BE THE FIRST *CASUALTY* OF THE COMING WAR.

WE *ALL WILL BE, LADY FREYJA*, UNLESS WE CAN STOP MALEKITH'S ARMIES FROM SPREADING REALM TO REALM.

I'M AFRAID WE DON'T HAVE A LOT OF RESOURCES RIGHT NOW, JANE. THERE'S NO MORE S.H.I.E.L.D. I'M AN *AGENT OF NOTHING*.

IT'S ALL WE CAN DO JUST TO KEEP THE ASGARDIAN *REFUGEES* AROUND HERE FED AND CARED FOR.

YOU DO THE WORK OF A SAINT, *ROSALIND SOLOMON*, BUT ALL WILL BE FOR NAUGHT IF WE CANNOT AID THOR.

YOU'RE RIGHT. I KNOW I HAVEN'T KNOWN HIM FOR LONG...

...BUT HE IS STILL MY *BROTHER IN BLOOD*, AND I KNOW HIS SOUL. AND I HAVE NEVER SEEN HIM LIKE THIS.

WHEN WE WERE PRISONERS OF THE ANGELS, THOR ASKED ME...IF I THOUGHT HE WAS *WORTHY*.

AND HOW DID YOU ANSWER, ANGELA?

I AM HERE FOR *ANSWERS*. AND YOU WILL GIVE THEM TO MY *HAMMER* HERE.

HOW IS MALEKITH MOVING HIS FORCES BETWEEN THE REALMS?!

AND WHERE ARE HIS ARMIES HEADED NEXT?!

SPEAK, ANGELS!

YOU'RE WASTING YOUR TIME, BROTHER. THESE HARPIES WOULD SWALLOW THEIR OWN TONGUES BEFORE THEY'D GIVE YOU ANSWERS.

NO MATTER HOW MUCH YOU THREATEN THEM, THEY'LL STILL BE MORE FRIGHTENED OF BETRAYING THEIR QUEEN AND THEIR REALM.

YOU'RE RIGHT, THOUGH. WE'RE IN NO POSITION TO TAKE PRISONERS. YET WE CAN'T JUST LET THESE WINGED SADISTS FLY FREE. SO WHAT DO WE DO WITH THEM?

THOR?

WE HAVE A PRISON, VALKYRIE. RIGHT HERE.

AND IF THESE ANGELS DO NOT FEAR MY HAMMER...

...THEN LET THEM SPEND *ETERNITY* BY ITS SIDE!

"HE FASTENED THE ENTIRE SHIP TO ONE OF HIS HAMMERS AND SENT IT FLYING INTO THE DEPTHS OF SPACE.

"ANGELS TRAPPED FOREVER IN THEIR OWN PRISON. I MUST SAY, IN THAT MOMENT...

"...MY BROTHER FELT LIKE A TRUE SON OF *ODIN*."

BROTHER. YOU ASKED ME A QUESTION EARLIER. I WOULD ANSWER IT NOW.

YOU ASKED IF YOU WERE WORTHY.

I WOULD LIKE TO TELL YOU YES. BUT I'M AFRAID I AM TOO SCARRED TO EVER BE THE ARBITER OF SUCH THINGS.

I AM NOT WORTHY OF CALLING YOU WORTHY, I SUPPOSE YOU COULD SAY. I CAN ONLY TELL YOU THIS:

YOU ARE THE BEATING HEART OF THE REALMS, THOR ODINSON. NOT JUST FOR ASGARD. FOR *ALL* OF THEM, WHETHER THEY WANT TO ADMIT IT OR NOT.

WITHOUT YOU, THE SKIES WOULD BE SILENT AND YGGDRASIL WOULD BE NOTHING BUT A GALLOWS HUNG WITH DEAD WORLDS. SO IF *YOU* ARE NOT WORTHY, BROTHER...

"...THEN WHAT THE HEL HOPE DO ANY OF THE REST OF US HAVE?"

AND WHAT DID THOR SAY TO THAT?

WHAT HE USUALLY SAYS, FREYJA.

KRAKAKOOOOM

"SO DOES ANYONE HAVE THE FAINTEST IDEA... WHERE MY SON IS AT THIS MOMENT?"

SO MANY HAMMERS.

BUT NONE OF THEM ARE YOU.

NONE OF THEM TELL ME WHAT TO DO.

OF COURSE, ALL-MOTHER, WE'VE GOT TO HELP THOR, BUT HE'S RIGHT TO BE WORRIED. THIS WAR WILL BE THE END OF US ALL.

AND I HAVE NO IDEA HOW TO BEGIN EVEN PREPARING TO--

KNOCK KNOCK

HOLD ON, I'M COMING.

9

THE WOMAN WITH THE VIBRANIUM GUN

...SO DID *I*.

TURNS OUT THERE ARE *OTHER* GUNS AND BADGES IN THE WORLD.

AND BOY, JUST WAIT'LL YOU SEE WHAT *THIS* ONE CAN DO.

...I BECAME SOMETHING ELSE.

S.H.I.E.L.D. IS DEAD. DESERVEDLY SO, MANY WOULD SAY. AND DEAD IT SHALL REMAIN.

HERE WE ARE NOT LOOKING TO RECREATE THE BUREAUCRATIC FOLLIES OF THE PAST.

ROZ SOLOMON.
FORMER AGENT OF S.H.I.E.L.D.

BEFORE BROXTON, I WAS AN ENVIRONMENTALIST. THE NIGHT IT FELL...

DAYS EARLIER.
WAKANDA.

OUR AGENTS WILL NOT BE THE POLICEMEN OF THE WORLD. AND OUR ORGANIZATION WILL NOT BE INFILTRATED OR MISUSED ON A DAILY BASIS.

NOT SO LONG AS I AM ALIVE AND STILL CAPABLE OF SWINGING A STICK.

FORGET EVERYTHING YOU EVER LEARNED FROM S.H.I.E.L.D.--THIS IS SOMETHING ENTIRELY NEW.

WELCOME TO THE *AGENTS OF WAKANDA.*

OKOYE.
LEADER OF THE *DORA MILAJE.*

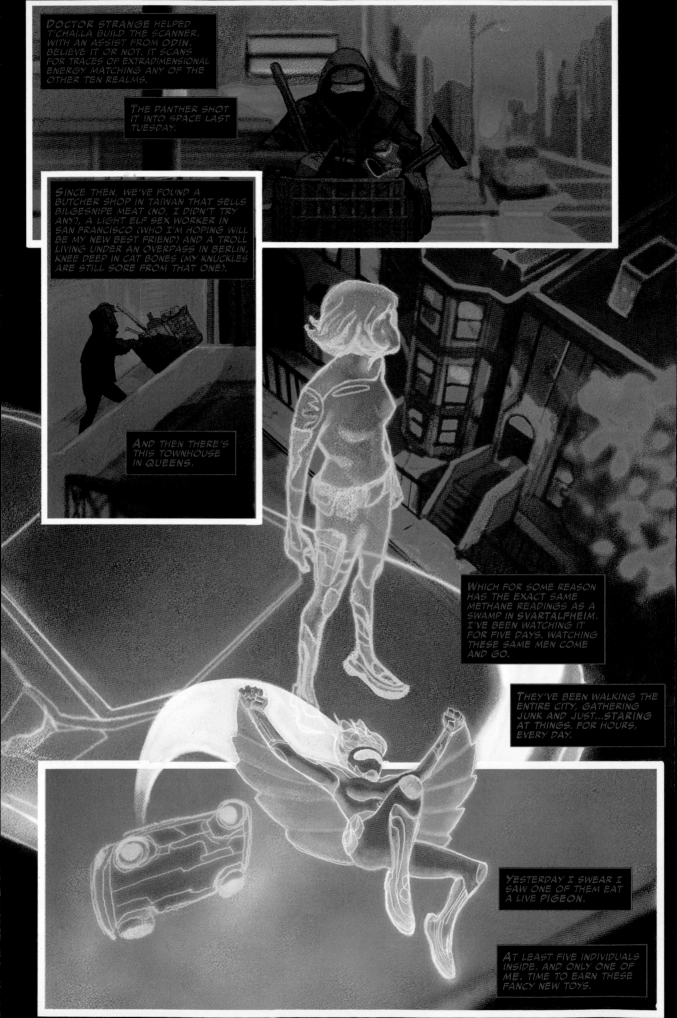

DOCTOR STRANGE HELPED T'CHALLA BUILD THE SCANNER. WITH AN ASSIST FROM ODIN, BELIEVE IT OR NOT. IT SCANS FOR TRACES OF EXTRADIMENSIONAL ENERGY MATCHING ANY OF THE OTHER TEN REALMS.

THE PANTHER SHOT IT INTO SPACE LAST TUESDAY.

SINCE THEN, WE'VE FOUND A BUTCHER SHOP IN TAIWAN THAT SELLS BILGESNIPE MEAT (NO, I DIDN'T TRY ANY), A LIGHT ELF SEX WORKER IN SAN FRANCISCO (WHO I'M HOPING WILL BE MY NEW BEST FRIEND) AND A TROLL LIVING UNDER AN OVERPASS IN BERLIN, KNEE DEEP IN CAT BONES (MY KNUCKLES ARE STILL SORE FROM THAT ONE).

AND THEN THERE'S THIS TOWNHOUSE IN QUEENS.

WHICH FOR SOME REASON HAS THE EXACT SAME METHANE READINGS AS A SWAMP IN SVARTALFHEIM. I'VE BEEN WATCHING IT FOR FIVE DAYS. WATCHING THESE SAME MEN COME AND GO.

THEY'VE BEEN WALKING THE ENTIRE CITY, GATHERING JUNK AND JUST...STARING AT THINGS. FOR HOURS, EVERY DAY.

YESTERDAY I SWEAR I SAW ONE OF THEM EAT A LIVE PIGEON.

AT LEAST FIVE INDIVIDUALS INSIDE. AND ONLY ONE OF ME. TIME TO EARN THESE FANCY NEW TOYS.

THE BRONX.

RIING RIING

HEY, *ROZ*, HOW'S THE FIRST WEEK ON THE JOB GO--

JANE! QUICK QUESTION!

YOU FOUGHT *FROST GIANTS* WHEN YOU WERE THOR, RIGHT?

YEAH, A FEW. WHAT'S ALL THAT *NOISE* IN THE BACKGROUND? YOU HAVING TARGET PRACTICE?

YES! GAGGH!

OCCUPIED

AND LET'S JUST SAY, HYPOTHETICALLY, THAT SOMEONE WAS LOOKING TO *BRING DOWN* A FROST GIANT. WHAT WOULD BE THE BEST WAY TO DO THAT?

ROZ. WHAT THE HELL ARE YOU DOING?

MY JOB!

BOOM!

BOOM!

BOOM!

GAGGH!!!

KILL HER!

UM, SURE, *JENNIFER.* I DIDN'T MEAN TO--

FOR *TRAINING.* LOTS OF TRAINING.

RIGHT, I REALLY DON'T NEED TO KNOW ANY--

LOUD TRAINING. VERY LOUD.

OKAY, I'M GONNA GO NOW.

HULK TIME NOW.

THOR BE *BUSY* FOR WHILE.

NO MATTER WHAT HEAR, NO COME INSIDE.

HULK *SMASH!*

HA, IS IT TRAINING TIME ALREADY? SMASH AWAY, MY LADY!

I REMEMBER THE FACES FROM THAT LAST NIGHT IN BROXTON. EVERY ONE OF THEM. LOOKING UP AT ME WITH SHOCK AND HORROR.

BUT NO ONE WAS MORE SHOCKED OR HORRIFIED THAN ME.

AS I SHOT AND KILLED THEM ALL.

HA HA HAA HAA!

ROZ!
SHE'S A SPY. KILL HER.
MALEKITH WILL WANT HER ALIVE. FOR A LITTLE WHILE AT LEAST.
I KNOW THIS FACE. I'VE SEEN IT BEFORE. THIS...HOLY STONES...
OH HELL. NOT TROLLS. NOT AGAIN.
WHAT THE HEL HAVE WE HERE?
THIS IS ROZ SOLOMON, THE TROLL SLAYER OF BROXTON.
YOU KILLED MY BROTHER, YOU HUMAN GARBAGE.
I'M GONNA GRIND YOUR FACE-FLESH BETWEEN MY BACK TEE--
BOOM!
BROXTON, OKLAHOMA, WAS WHERE THE GODS USED TO LIVE.

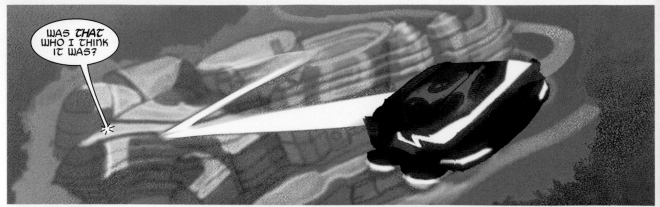

WAS *THAT* WHO I THINK IT WAS?

I'M QUITE SURE I HAVE NO IDEA WHAT THOUGHTS GO THROUGH YOUR HEAD, *ULIK*.

THAT WAS ROZ SOLOMON, THE TROLL SLAYER OF BROXTON.

IF WE WEREN'T UNDER ORDERS FROM MALEKITH TO LIE LOW, I WOULD'VE TORN HER TO BLOODY SHREDS.

NEXT TIME, BE MY GUEST.

GET UP, AGGER. BOSS WANTS TO SEE YOU.

I'M UNDER HOUSE ARREST.

YOU THINK MALEKITH GIVES A DAMN ABOUT MIDGARD LAWS?

BESIDES, WE'RE NOT EXACTLY WALKING OUT THE FRONT DOOR.

WE HAVE OUR OWN BIFROST, AFTER ALL.

NOW COME THE *HEL* ON.

WE'VE ALL GOT A *WAR* TO PLAN.

10

A BOY AND HIS ALL-FATHER

I WASN'T THERE WHEN THE BOY WAS BORN. OR IF I WAS, I WAS TOO DAMNED **DRUNK** TO REMEMBER.

THIS IS NOT A DISCUSSION. YOU WILL GO. YOUR **ALL-FATHER** COMMANDS YOU.

I HAVEN'T ALWAYS BEEN THERE SINCE. BUT HEL, WHEN HAS HE EVER LISTENED TO A WORD I'VE SAID ANYWAY?

WHY NOT JUST KILL ME **YOURSELF**, BROTHER, RIGHT HERE AND NOW? THAT'D SURE BE A DAMN SIGHT EASIER.

AND A HEL OF A LOT MORE NOBLE THAN LEAVING IT UP TO THE DAMNED **DARK ELVES**.

I AM **ODIN**, SON OF BOR. THE HIGH HOLY LORD OF ASGARD. THE ALMIGHTY ALL-GOD.

I AM THE WILL, THE WORD AND THE ONE-EYED WRATH.

TAKE THAT RUSTY OLD SPEAR OF YOURS AND STAB IT RIGHT THROUGH MY HEART! THAT'S THE ALL-FATHER WAY!

THAT'S WHAT **BOR** WOULD'VE DONE!

BUT OVER THE EONS I'VE BEGRUDGINGLY COME TO LEARN...THAT EVEN OMNIPOTENCE HAS ITS LIMITS.

JUST BECAUSE I'M THE ALL-FATHER DOESN'T MEAN I KNOW HOW TO DO EVERY BLASTED THING.

LIKE HOW TO BE A **FATHER**.

I'M NOT TRYING TO KILL YOU, **CUL**. NO MATTER HOW MUCH YOU MIGHT DESERVE IT.

I'M TRYING TO GIVE YOU ONE LAST CHANCE TO REDEEM YOURSELF, BROTHER, AND HOPEFULLY SAVE US ALL.

FATHER. I SEE YOU'RE KEEPING BUSY.

AYE, SHOWED THESE DWARVES HOW TO FORGE. THEN HOW TO DRINK.

WAS MAKING YOU A WEAPON. AROUND HERE SOMEWHERE.

TALK TO THE BOY.

I DO HOPE YOU DIDN'T KILL THE DWARVES. I'M RUNNING LOW ON HAMMERS.

HE LOOKS TIRED. STRETCHED TOO THIN. IN NEED OF HELP.

AYE. I HEARD ABOUT THAT MESS WITH YOUR SISTER.

THAT ONE'S ALWAYS BEEN TROUBLE. YOU TRY TO RAISE THEM RIGHT, BUT WHAT WOULD THEY HAVE YOU DO? PAY THE RANSOM EVERY TIME THEY'RE KIDNAPPED BY ANGELS? HRRPH.

I SHOULD TELL HIM WHAT I KNOW.

SIT. GRAB YOURSELF A DRINK, BOY.

THAT I'VE SENT CUL TO SVARTALFHEIM. THAT MALEKITH HAS BUILT HIS OWN BIFROST AND WILL SURELY USE IT TO INVADE ALL OF--

I CAME FOR HAMMERS.

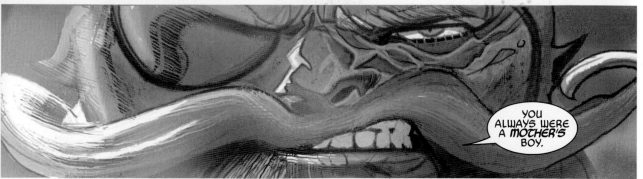

YOU ALWAYS WERE A MOTHER'S BOY.

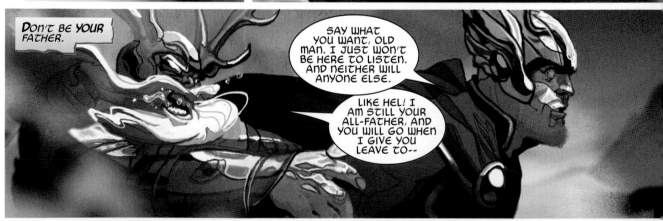

SLAP!

FATHER.

THE REALMS HAVE PASSED YOU BY.

LET THEM.

AND STAY OUT OF EVERYONE'S WAY.

THOR. BEFORE YOU GO...

I FOUND THAT *HAMMER* I MADE YOU.

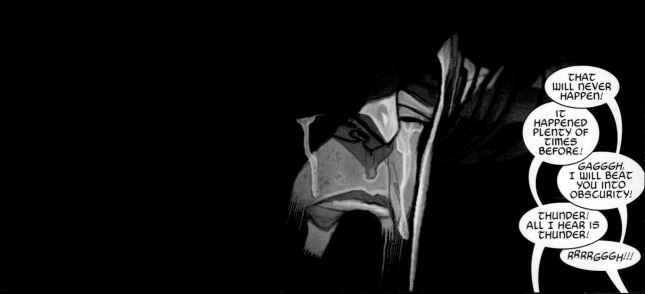

BELIEVE ME, I KNOW ROCK BOTTOM WHEN I SEE IT. I'VE BEEN THERE.
TELL ME WHEN IT STARTED.
I INVENTED MEAD.
OKAY. THIS IS GONNA TAKE A WHILE.
MY NAME IS ODIN BORSON. ALL-FATHER OF ASGARD.
BUT LET ME NOT BE REMEMBERED AS SUCH.
AS THE WORST ALL-FATHER WHO EVER SAT THE THRONE OF THE REALM ETERNAL.

LET ME BE REMEMBERED SIMPLY AS A FATHER.
OF THE GREATEST GOD WHO EVER LIVED.
EVEN IF THE ONLY THING I EVER TRULY TAUGHT THE BOY...
...WAS NOT TO BE LIKE ME.

11

THE EVE OF WAR

I WOKE IN TEARS FROM A DREAM LAST NIGHT.

A DREAM OF FIRE.

A GREAT FOREST WAS ENGULFED IN FLAMES. SO TOWERING THEY SCORCHED THE SKY.

A FOREST OF BURNING TEMPLES. AND SCREAMING GODS.

I KNEW THIS WAS NO MERE DREAM. EVEN FROM ACROSS THE FORMLESS GULF BETWEEN REALMS, I COULD FEEL THAT SOMETHING TRULY HORRENDOUS HAD TRANSPIRED.

MIGHTY VANAHEIM HAS FALLEN.

LAST REFUGE OF THE RECLUSIVE VANIR, THE GREAT GODS OF OLD. THE REALM OF MY BIRTH. AND NORNS HELP US...

I KNOW IT WILL NOT BE THE LAST REALM TO BURN.

He did not even know he was doing it.

OH MY GOD. GO FASTER!

For days, the weather across Midgard had been chaotic--reflecting the tumultuous mood of the God of Thunder.

IT'S TOO LATE, WE'RE NOT GONNA--

The tsunami that hit the islands of Hawaii came without warning. But the prayers of the drowning that followed were quickly answered with a rumble of thunder.

KRAKODOOM

'TIS THE HEART THAT BEATS INSIDE HIS CHEST.

NOTHING IN ALL THE REALMS IS STRONGER THAN THE HEART OF THOR.

THIS WAY! TO THE SAFETY OF DRY GROUND! *THIS WAY TO LIFE!*

I PRAY HE HASN'T FORGOTTEN THAT.

I PRAY THOR HASN'T FORSAKEN HIMSELF. FOR HIS OWN SAKE.

FOR ALL OUR SAKES.

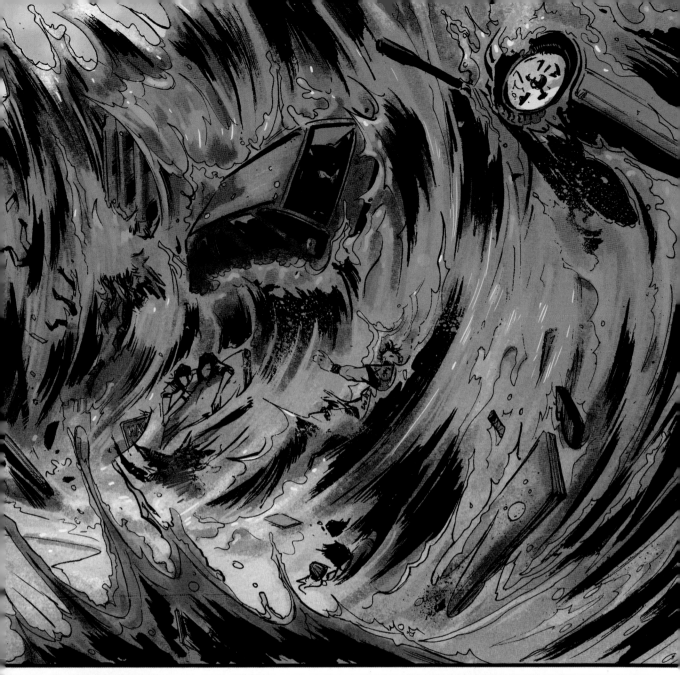

FOR THE SAKE OF THE REALMS.

BY THE GRACE OF THOR WE WILL BE SAVED. MORTAL AND GOD ALIKE. THIS I HAVE KNOWN, IN THE VERY DEPTHS OF MY SOUL...

...FOR A VERY LONG TIME.

MANY YEARS AGO. MIDGARD.

HER NAME WAS *ERIKA THE RED.* FIERCEST VIKING WHO EVER LIVED.

SHE'S IN VALHALLA WITH THE VALKYRIES NOW. PERHAPS SOMEDAY, I'LL SEE HER AGAIN.

I AM SO DEEPLY SORRY, MY SON. SHE MUST HAVE BEEN QUITE AN AMAZING WOMAN. I WISH I COULD HAVE MET HER IN LIFE.

AYE. I WISH THAT AS WELL, LADY FREYJA.

I BROUGHT YOU HERE SO YOU WOULD SEE...THAT I AM NOT THE PETTY CHILD FATHER THINKS I AM. NOT ALWAYS, AT LEAST.

I LISTENED TO YOU, MOTHER. 'TIS IMPORTANT TO ME THAT YOU KNOW THAT.

MY BELOVED BOODLE. I KNOW WELL WHAT MANNER OF CHILD YOU ARE.

DO YOU REMEMBER? THE LAST TIME YOU FOUND ME TRYING TO LIFT THE HAMMER, YOU SAID...

"FORGET WORTHY. FIND *LOVE*."

AND I DID, MOTHER. I WANTED YOU TO KNOW THAT I DID. FOR A TIME AT LEAST.

OH MY SON, YOU ARE SO VERY LOVED. I ADORE YOU WITH ALL THE HEART OF A GODDESS.

"FROM NOW UNTIL THE END OF TIME."

UNTOLD EONS FROM NOW.
THE ASGARD AT THE END OF EVERYTHING.

I WASN'T, FRIGG.

I WAS.

WELL HE'S NOT. HE'S *THOR.* HE'LL OUTLIVE THE STARS.

HE ALREADY HAS. MOST OF THEM ARE *DYING TOO,* REMEMBER?

HE'S *NOT DEAD.* DON'T EVEN *THINK* IT.

THE UNIVERSE ITSELF IS BREATHING ITS LAST. AND NOT EVEN ALL-FATHER THOR CAN SAVE IT.

STOP SAYING THAT ABOUT POP-POP, ELLISIV! HE'S THE STRONGEST GRANDFATHER EVER! HE SAVED MIDGARD ALL BY HIMSELF!

HE DID, ATLI. AND DEFEATED THE MOST POWERFUL DOCTOR DOOM WHO EVER LIVED. OUR ALL-GRANDFATHER HAS EARNED HIS REST.

WAR.

GRANDFATHER! HE *IS* ALIVE!

IS HE? HE STILL *LOOKS* DEAD.

WAR IS COMING. THE WAR OF THE REALMS.

THE WAR OF THE REALMS? BUT THAT'S *ANCIENT HISTORY.* HE MUST BE DELIRIOUS.

WAR. SO MANY WILL FALL. AND *MIDGARD...* MIDGARD WILL NEED...

"...DON'T WE ALL."

HOW DO YOU FEEL, JANE?

McCARTHY MEDICAL INSTITUTE
MARIA WHEELOCK CANCER CENTER

Medical Record
FOSTER, JANE

HONESTLY, LIKE I HAVEN'T FELT IN A VERY LONG TIME, DOC. LIKE I'M ACTUALLY GETTING *BETTER*...

YOU'RE NOT JUST GETTING BETTER...

THE LATEST ROUND OF BLOOD TESTS AND IMAGING ALL SHOW NO FINDINGS. THERE'S *NO EVIDENCE* OF THE *CANCER* LEFT IN YOUR LIVER OR REMAINING LYMPH NODES.

WE'LL WANT TO KEEP DOING REGULAR TESTS, BUT... I'D SAY YOU'RE DONE WITH CHEMO AND RADIOTHERAPY, JANE FOSTER.

YOU BEAT THE ODDS. YOU DID IT.

J. REICHERT

YOU'RE IN *COMPLETE* REMISSION.

JANE?

DID YOU HEAR WHAT I JUST SAID?

KRRDDDAKDOOOOM

WAS THAT *THUNDER?* DAMN WEATHERMEN DON'T KNOW NOTHING.

YOU HEAR ABOUT VANAHEIM?

AYE. I HEARD. PROTECT YOUR FLANK.

I KNOW YOU HAVE A LOT OF FRIENDS THERE AMONG THE VANIR. I'M SORRY, LADY SIF. DO YOU HAVE ANY IDEA... IF THEY'RE...

THEY'RE ALL DEAD.

AS FAR AS I'M CONCERNED. THEY HAVE TO BE. SINCE NONE OF THEM CAN HELP US IN THE FIGHT TO COME.

FOCUS ON *THAT*, BRUNNHILDE. ON THE *TRAINING*. WE MUST BE *READY*.

I'M A *VALKYRIE*. IT'S MY *JOB* TO CARE ABOUT THE *DEAD*.

WELL, THEN YOU'RE IN LUCK, VALKYRIE.

FOR THESE STREETS WILL SOON BE LITTERED WITH THEM.

"HE'S NOT COMING, MOTHER."

"HE'S LATE. BUT HE *WILL* BE HERE."

"THOR VOWED THAT HE WOULD COME WHEN HE WAS FINISHED REGAINING CONTROL OF MIDGARD'S WEATHER.

I MADE ALL HIS FAVORITES. MUTTON AND OXTAILS AND LAMB SHANKS..."

"THORI HERE. CAN THORI EAT?"

"BAH?"

"MOTHER..."

"BY THE GRACE OF THOR WE WILL BE SAVED. I STILL BELIEVE THAT WITH ALL MY HEART. BUT IF IT COMES TO IT...

...MY *OWN* GRACE IS SOMETHING TO BE RECKONED WITH AS WELL."

"HE'LL BE HERE, BALDER. WE HAVEN'T LOST HIM.

HE'S NOT HIS *FATHER.*"

"NOT YET."

I'M NOT MY FATHER.

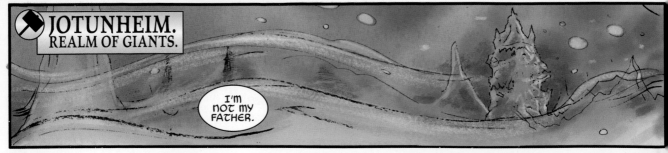

THAT MUCH IS CLEAR. IF I *WERE*...IF I WERE THAT GIANT AND POWERFUL...I COULD END THIS WAR MYSELF IN ONE BLOODY EVENING.

BUT I AM JUST *ONE LOKI*. AND WHAT HAS THAT EVER GOTTEN ME?

A COZY LITTLE MOUSE HOLE IN MY FATHER'S FRIGID CASTLE.

I'M SORRY. I TRULY AM.

I THOUGHT I COULD STOP MALEKITH *MY WAY.* BUT NOW IT'S TOO *LATE.* I STABBED YOU IN THE BACK FOR *NOTHING,* LADY FREYJA.

WHAT HAPPENS NOW WAS NEVER WHAT I INTENDED, BUT JUST KNOW...

...IT'S MOST *ASSUREDLY* WHAT I *DESERVE.*

EVEN IF IT BE THE END OF *ME*.

IF THAT HAPPENS...

...I WILL *JOIN* YOU IN FIRE, MJOLNIR.

AND WE'LL BE REUNITED AT LAST, MY FRIEND.

UNTIL THEN...

...THOR HAS A WAR TO FIGHT.

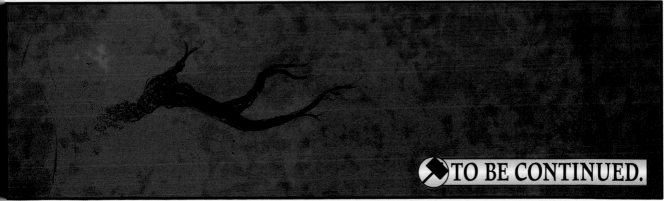

TO BE CONTINUED.

#1 VARIANT
BY **CHRISTIAN WARD**

#1 VARIANT
BY **KAARE ANDREWS**

#2 YOUNG GUNS VARIANT
BY **RUSSELL DAUTERMAN** & **MATTHEW WILSON**

#2 VARIANT
BY **MIKE DEODATO JR.** & **FRANK MARTIN**

#1 DESIGN VARIANT
BY **RUSSELL DAUTERMAN**

#1 REMASTERED VARIANT
BY **JACK KIRBY**, **VINCE COLLETTA**
& **PAUL MOUNTS** WITH **MICHAEL KELLEHER**

#1–5 COMBINED VARIANT COVERS
BY **JAMES HARREN** & **DAVE STEWART**

#5 COSMIC GHOST RIDER VS. VARIANT
BY **EMA LUPACCHINO** & **JASON KEITH**

#6 MARVEL KNIGHTS VARIANT
BY **RICHARD ISANOVE**

#8 VARIANT
BY **KAARE ANDREWS**

#8 CONAN VS. VARIANT
BY **PATCH ZIRCHER** & **DEAN WHITE**

#9 CONAN VS. VARIANT
BY **GREG SMALLWOOD**

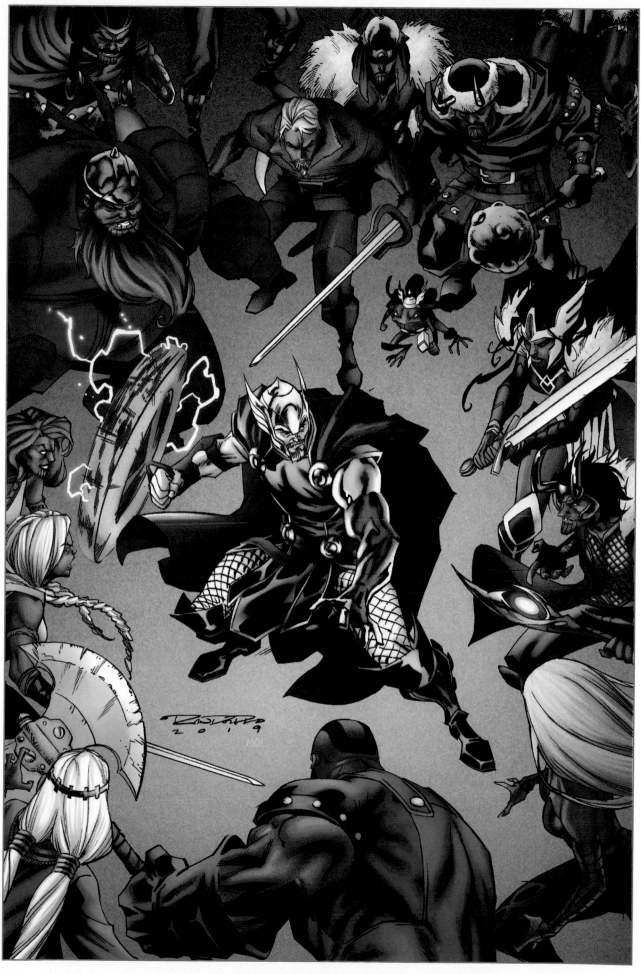

#10 SKRULLS VARIANT
BY **KHARY RANDOLPH** & **MORRY HOLLOWELL**

#11 VARIANT
BY **GIUSEPPE CAMUNCOLI** & **JASON KEITH**

#7, #9-10 COVER SKETCHES
BY **MIKE DEL MUNDO**

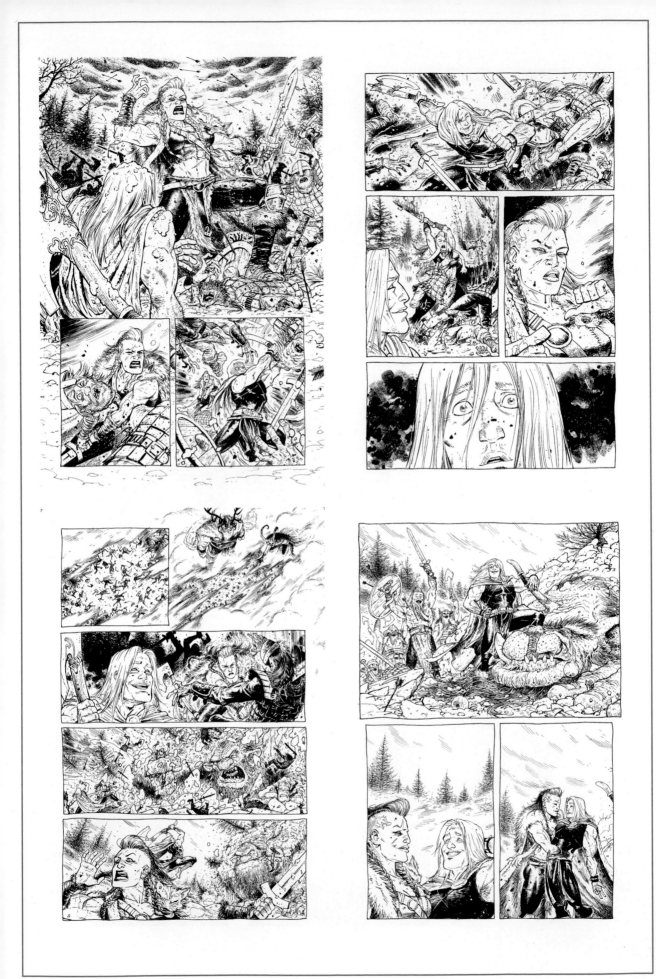

#7, PAGES 8-11 ART
BY **TONY MOORE**

ERIKA THE RED & VIKING LOKI SKETCHES
BY **TONY MOORE**

#8 LAYOUTS
BY **MIKE DEL MUNDO**

GLOVES GUN LIGHTS UP,
LIGHT UP WAKANDA
WAKANDA TECH TYPE
TECH PATTERNS
PATTERNS

ROZ WAKANDA WHIP

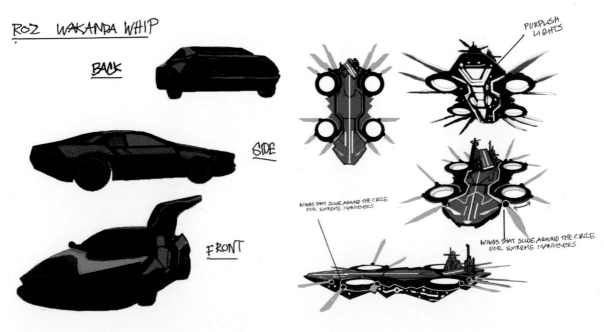

BACK

SIDE

FRONT

PURPLISH LIGHTS

WINGS THAT SLIDE AROUND THE CIRCLE FOR EXTREME MANUEVERS

WINGS THAT SLIDE AROUND THE CIRCLE FOR EXTREME MANUEVERS

AGENT ROZ SOLOMON & WAKANDAN VEHICLE SKETCHES
BY **MIKE DEL MUNDO**